Pain Behind the Smile

Leah Hulan

Eggman Publishing, Inc.

For interviews and other information call:
1-800-409-7277

ISBN: 1-886371-01-6

Eggman Publishing, Inc.
2909 Poston Avenue, Suite 203
Nashville, TN 37203
(615) 327-9390

Dedication

I dedicate this book to you—the reader—and to all the suffering people of our often crazy and confusing world who are struggling with an addiction. If you are one of those unfortunates who is suffering, know that you are not alone in your darkness and pain. And if you suffer not, may you read with compassion for all of us who do.

Contents

Preface

I have been on a voyage into darkness, a journey that sometimes still calls my name, begging me to return to its vile depths, a return that would certainly signal my decent into hell.

And not just figuratively.

My doctors have told me that if I do not escape this disease that has had its hold on me for more than half my life, I will die.

My heart, my lungs, my liver and all the other vital organs which hide behind my smile just can't take anymore.

But I want to live.

And writing this, seeing the details in black and white, is one way I hope to do battle against this dark force inside me.

If my words help another soul who knows my pain, it will be the ultimate slap in the face to this disease, something I would forever treasure.

But the cold, selfish truth is that I am writing these words to help me first, then the next person, and then the next, if that is possible.

For that selfish reason, you must know that I wrote this journal without thought to organization or rationalization, neither of which are traits of the disease that I have allowed to hold me captive for so long.

So, please remember I make no claim that my words "make sense" to anyone but me.

Simply, I have written down my feelings, when and how I felt them, so my words aren't always orderly, polished and smooth.

But, of course, that is the final irony.

Order is something that doesn't exist in the darkness where I have lived for so many years, a place where it's often difficult to tell up from down, wakefulness from nightmares or heaven from hell.

A special thank you to my dear friend "Doc" for believing in me and for helping me to turn dreams into realities. You are truly a blessing and have helped me find value within myself.

To my "powerful" hero, SGT Dan McCraw, my best friends Tracy Bankston and Michelle Curl, and to all my counselors in treatment—especially Lori, Gretta, and Nancy from Mountain View Recovery Center, Thank you for not giving up on me. Also, to my beautiful and beloved family, my sisters Lori and Kara, my grandmother Mamay, and my mother Marcia, thank you for your unconditional love and support. You are the invaluable jewels of my world.

A hear-felt thank you to Wes Yoder and Ron Miller of Ambassador Speakers' Bureau for believing in me and granting me the opportunity to share my struggles of my disease and my growth in the Lord with others.

To Richard Courtney of Eggman Publishing I owe my deepest appreciation for his recognition that my own struggle to find myself within the dementia of my addictive eating disorder could also help others who may be suffering from this disease or even other addictions as well.

To the beautiful and most talented Susan Thomas, I dedicate my eternal gratitude for her skill and compassion in editing my book. God was certainly smiling on me the night that I met her!

For information regarding appearances and speeches, please contact Ron Miller, Director of Operations, AMBASSADOR Speakers Bureau, P.O. Box 50358, Nashville, TN 37205, (615) 377-9100, Fax: (615) 661-4344.

For information regarding *Pain Behind the Smile* please contact Richard Courtney, Eggman Publishing, Inc., 2909 Poston Avenue, Suite 203, Nashville, TN 37203, (615) 327-9390, Fax: (615) 327-9150.

Chapter One

Demons of the Past

Tiny beads of sweat spread across my forehead, creeping down my face and neck.

My eyes burned from the intense strain of the deep heaves coming up from my chest, making even the tiniest veins in my head throb so violently it seemed my head would explode.

My heart was racing uncontrollably, throwing my whole body into a rack of constant, shaking spasms.

With each new convulsion, the smothering cramps in my esophagus sent tight ropes of pain around my heart, creating renewed fear that I was about to experience another one of my anxiety riddled mini heart attacks.

But any realistic reasoning in my head, which was dangling like a wet mop above the rim of the toilet bowl, was powerless.

Once begun, there was no turning back from the convulsions of vomiting, once I initiated them.

And neither the fear of death nor thoughts of all the irreparable damage and destruction I was subjecting my body to — over and over again, day after day, year after year — could penetrate the chaotic web of confusion I was lost in, a web woven by my demons of the past into an omnipotent addiction.

For more than twelve years, I had done everything to overlook the stark reality of the dark depths of my disease.

I did not question the how or the why I had allowed myself to slip so far down. And if one of those questions began sneaking up on me, I consistently and successfully buried them inside my deteriorating soul — shoving them down and burying them beneath the gross amounts of food I incessantly and ritually consumed.

Of course, within minutes, I would again be racing to the bathroom where I would lock the world outside in order to propel the mountains of food out of my throat almost as quickly as I had stuffed it down.

Thus, this moment I was back again, face to face with my secret lover, the toilet bowl, blinded by streaming tears as I clutched my stomach with my sweaty, trembling hands.

But for once, my lover seemed suddenly unkind, making me dizzier and dizzier as I watched the swirling water continue its course down the porcelain pit. And as each second passed, breathing became difficult and my heartbeat was jagged, becoming more and more irregular.

I was panicking, but not from the physical pain.

I was panicking — just knowing there was still food left in my stomach!

Having already thrown up three times, I still had not been able to completely rid my body of all the food.

I could feel it.

And in my mind, I was convinced any food I allowed my body to actually digest would act as a toxin, poisoning me more lethally every second I failed to vomit it up.

My merciless mind did not stop there. Beyond the physical terrors of pain and panic, it relentlessly screamed at me, telling me what a very bad and vile girl I was for having allowed myself the wicked luxury of eating in the first place!

"You are despicable, Leah!" my mind shrieked over an internal loud-speaker. "Get rid of the food, now, you horrible, horrible girl!"

I mustered enough energy to heave again.

I coughed. I choked. I pounded my stomach with my fists. I did everything I knew to make myself vomit again, all the tricks I knew so well, but I still couldn't seem to get it all up!

What was going on? After so many years of purging 15 to 20 times a day, what was the problem now?

Frantic with fear that I would be unable to vomit again, leaving at least some of the food I had just devoured inside me, I struggled to get a hold of my panic.

I stood, then paced back and forth across the bathroom floor.

"Slow down!" I scolded myself. "You're forgetting the ritual! You know it's a rhythm thing!

"Just drink some warm water real fast, count to eight, then bend over quickly and heave again! And if that doesn't work, walk around in circles, or jump up and down if you have to!

"Whatever, it takes, you had better get rid of it all this time ... or you'll have to stay locked in this bathroom until you do!"

It worked, even though the biting sensation of cold toilet water splashing up on my face as I purged again was embarrassing and nasty.

But even those humbling feelings of degradation were minuscule compared to the powerful "high" that came as my "reward" for purging.

Bizarre as it may seem, vomiting stimulates sensations in the part of the brain that governs the sense of pleasure, something I had stumbled on that served only to enhance my addiction to purging.

So, as usual, that high made me feel like a "good" girl, at least temporarily once again. I quickly washed my face and hands, wiping away both the sweat and the shakes. Then I touched up my make-up, preparing to leave the all too familiar confinement of my bathroom.

But something was different this time, this moment.

I couldn't leave.

My mind started thinking, a dangerous thing that could threaten my blindness to my disease, but I couldn't stop it.

Somehow, I realized I had unconsciously become addicted, not only to my purging "highs," but also to the sense of power I experienced by controlling my food and manipulating my weight.

Never, not from the youngest memories of my youth, had I ever seemed to be able to control anything around me.

Somebody else had always controlled it all.

How to act. What to say. What not to say. Where I lived. When I got to see the people I really loved. What other people said to me. What other people did to my mind. What other people did to my body.

I was helpless.

So, through my self-indulgence of accepting my fate as a victim, I reasoned that if I couldn't control anything else around me, then at least I would exert control over my food.

With that, I had the power to reward, as well as the power to punish myself.

I was in control, at last!

I could focus on surface issues such as weight, food and body image and never have to deal with the demons of my past that fed my addiction and disease.

I could hide the living hell I had created from everyone, even rationalize it to myself, because it was safe for me. I knew what to expect, no surprises and no feelings. I could exist outside the bathroom door — doing whatever needed to be done in the eyes of others — until the next eating frenzy, without ever having to endure the frightening feelings of actually living.

I could hide in the isolation and security that my devilish disease provided me. With all my thoughts obsessed with food, I had no time to dwell on the past, so I was free from harm!

Or so I had thought.

But for the moment, I just wanted to make sure my dinner guests did not discover what I had been doing for the past 15 minutes. I had told them I had to fix my contacts, an excuse that always worked because it also camouflaged the real reason why my nose and eyes were always moist and watering.

And as I looked into the mirror to check my make-up one last time, I was able to ignore the harsh reality of all that had just happened when I saw my own image smiling back at me.

"Don't worry, Leah!" my sadistic mind coached. "Sure, you were bad to eat a meal tonight. You didn't run or work out today either, and remember you ate a sandwich two days ago that I had not given you permission to have. You didn't deserve to eat a single morsel tonight — especially that salad!

"But, don't worry. You can still redeem yourself.

"Just keep trying to be strong! Use your willpower! Don't be so weak! But since you've been bad now, you can't have anything else to eat for a week! You know you need to lose that 10 pounds! Guess you'll have to run about five or six miles tonight after everyone leaves. Also, you can get up at 5:30 in the morning and commence your cardiovascular routine. If you work-out for over three hours then, perhaps that will make up for your intolerable behavior tonight."

As I stared at the reflection looking back at me in the bathroom mirror and heard my mind's harsh words, I suddenly felt lost, alone, scared. My self-image had become so warped and twisted over the past years of mental, physical, and sexual abuse, I barely recognized the smiling girl in the mirror as me.

"What am I doing to myself?" I asked aloud. "Why do I torture myself? Why do I have to try so hard to be perfect?

"I am so tired, tired of trying to live with myself and all the pain."

Forgetting I had guests waiting outside, I sat down on the cold tiles of the bathroom floor, holding my knees close to my chest and began to rock myself for comfort. That's what I had done when I was little after being whipped or beaten to help me fall asleep to escape.

Now, warm tears filled my eyes again and flowed down my cheeks. I looked up at the wooden rafters and pretended I was outside under the divine protection of the glistening stars. Being outside, for reasons I had yet to discover, always made me feel free, free from the chains of my past that kept me bound to those haunting memories.

I slipped all the way down on the floor, laying my perspiring face against the clammy, cold tiles. The moistness cooled my throbbing head and refreshed my spirit.

Soon, I felt untroubled in my safe, little world of my own. Soothed into a daze by the gentle sound of running water in the sink I had left on to conceal my secret, I vanished into my dreams.

I was lost in the fields of my youth, running along the cow paths to the creek. In harmony with nature, I felt free and unrestricted! Here, there were no boundaries nor limits! I could flee from the unpleasantness of home and villains within my mind! I could run as far as I could see across the rolling hills and pastures of green!

Often, when I was young, I would run and run and run — just to test my own strength, like a newborn colt. I would pretend that someday, I would grow up to be a strong, beautiful horse, blessed with unyielding power! As I galloped across the fields in my own race to be noticed and to be the best, the vibrant sound of my hooves rhythmically pounded the earth, alerting the other animals that I was nearby to protect them. I dreamed that I was truly powerful and significant, but most of all loved, unbridled and free!

In my childhood, I remember running toward the creek, the warm sun in my face. I could feel the thistles harmlessly slapping my legs and knees with sharp little stings. I could actually feel the playful wind blowing through my hair and pushing against my back, driving me farther and farther away from the darkness of home. The smell of wild honeysuckle and fresh hay flirted with my nose and stimulated my senses, and the birds gleefully singing in the trees and dogs barking in the distant valley comforted me. And down by the creek, the soft gurgle of the water gently rolling over the rocky sandbar soothed me, inviting me to splash around in its shallow waters.

Here, the innocent, wild creatures of the land were my friends and became my closest confidants as I shared with them my most shameful secrets. We endured many a day and many a night together. I relied on them to listen to my plans of escape. Yet, since they had no need to escape anything, their only encouragement was that they couldn't criticize my quest to be someone that made a difference.

So I dreamed of being significant. I was so tired of being invisible and unheard. If only I could really become someday that beautiful and powerful horse of my make-believe world! I would make a difference! I promised I would.

So, this was my world, down by the creek. This was my world of salvation, my world of love and peace. This was my safe haven, in actuality and also in my mind. I really felt that God had to listen to my prayers there!

Life seemed so uncomplicated along the banks of my little creek.

Abruptly back on the bathroom floor, I was startled to reality by my sister, Kara, banging on the bathroom door.

"Hurry up!" she yelled. "What's wrong with you? We've got to go!"

Still confused from the sudden interruption and a bit upset by having to leave my dreams, I reluctantly picked myself up from the floor and glared into the mirror once again.

But it was black!

Shaking my head and blinking my eyes in an effort to focus, I looked into the mirror once more.

I could see my body. I could see my face. But my entire image was shrouded in black!

Only minutes before, I had acknowledged my illness and my warped body image and had come very close to realizing how sick I truly was. Now, peering into the mirror, I became lost in disgust with my detestable image.

But now, as fast as my blinking eyes, I had slammed the door on any realistic approach to admitting to myself the severity of my disease. And I was instantly back, up to my neck, in my addiction and in my denial.

"I'm so incredibly fat! I hate being fat!" I thought before asking myself harshly:

"Who is ever going to love you, Leah? You don't deserve to marry Tom. You have really been lucky to have been loved by him this long. But when he finds out about your past, he, too, will hate you! Just like I hate you, Leah!

"Why couldn't you have known? Why didn't you stop what those people did to your body? It's all your fault! If you really love Tom, leave him so you don't make your never-ending nightmare his reality, too!"

The transition into my make-believe world down by the creek had come accompanied with long forgotten memories and feelings, many of which I had vowed never to recollect again.

However, lately my dreams had regressed me too far into these forbidden dwellings locked in my mind and were causing me to remember things that I had long ago tried to block from my consciousness, forever. Thus, these surfacing, but still unconscious realizations of my past, were more than I was prepared to deal with, and once again I was back in a complete state of denial in order to protect myself and feel safe from the truth.

Emotionally spent and scared, I reacted by doing what I always did to feel as if I had some sense of control — purging food from my body.

Thus, bending over the toilet one more time, I heaved.

Proud, yet again of another "success," I quickly brushed my teeth and left the bathroom.

Greeting my sister and the other dinner guests with the wide smile they knew so well and had learned to expect, no one suspected a thing nor questioned me why I had been locked in the bathroom — for more than thirty 30 minutes.

My pain, my shame and my demons were safe from discovery one more time, one more day.

That "gal who has it all" could just smile and trick the world, as well as herself, into believing that life was easy and grand.

But how much longer could my body resist the self destruction?

And how much longer could I pretend?

6

Chapter Two

Day of Reckoning

The darkness was cold and suffocating.

My breath was being sucked out of my lungs like a vacuum by some kind of intangible force. I began to shiver incessantly, and I lost most feeling throughout my weakening body. Sudden flashes of intense light were making me dizzy and confused. Piercing sounds of frantic laughter and screams echoed in my ears. I felt my body being slowly dragged from the safety of my own bed into a more profound darkness.

Everything became silent. Suddenly, as I struggled to my feet, a vicious wind mysteriously appeared. Sweeping me off my feet and into the frigid air, the blustering tempest rapidly hurled my body into flight!

I screamed, but there was no sound. I fought, but there was no attacker.

I felt helpless as my body was wildly touched and grasped by hundreds of invisible hands as I sped through space. Twisting and turning to evade the painful sensations, I became inextricably disoriented.

"Where am I? What is happening to me? I hope it's not him again! Please go away! I'm just trying to sleep!"

Against all my will and all the strength I could muster, the tumultuous wind continued its savage attack of my body. The spanking breeze slapped and whipped me into unconsciousness as I uncontrollably sailed through the freezing, cold air. I awoke to the torturous pelting of hail and rain but had no defense against the ferocious assault!

Beaten up and dripping wet, I haphazardly scanned my surroundings, hoping to gain some sense of my location. But the endless darkness devoured the entire vicinity, preventing any recognition of the room. Groping blindly around with my hands, I perceived that I was laying upon a hard, uncomfortable bed of some sort, perhaps even a shrouded alter.

Futilely, I tried to get off the perch and stand, but there was an unyielding force on top of me, pinning me painfully down on my back. I tried to jostle off the force with my arms and legs, but they were numb, powerless.

Breathless, I was suddenly overwhelmed by a baffling and quite barbaric sensation — the most secret part of my body was being penetrated!

The wicked confusion perplexed my senses and left me almost comatose. I tried to scream, but there was no sound.

At the endless mercy of this violating power, I wanted desperately to know where I was!

I blinked my eyes hysterically, seeking to focus on anything at all! But I could see nothing. Neither could I understand what was happening. I closed my eyes tightly and prayed for escape. But my arms and legs were still paralyzed — there was no escape!

Overwhelmed with fear and confusion and unable to tolerate the unbeknown force a second longer, I marshalled every bit of energy I had left and pulled myself off the bed.

Slowly, I dragged my limp body down the long, black corridor towards the only light I detected. And although the asphyxiating force was still upon me, my strength prevailed and allowed me enough use of my arms to drag my body along through the cold darkness.

It took hours to reach the light! But once there, I stretched my hands toward the brightness, feeling its warmth seep through my fingertips and spread throughout my body!

Thinking I was safe and that the pain was over, I began to sob uncontrollably. Against the fading force, I had actually managed to escape, directly into the light!

So warmly and happily surprised, I found myself outside on the balcony of a grand, white, ante-bellum mansion. It could have been Scarlett O'Hara's safe and secure, beloved Tara!

But suddenly, screams of laughter flooded the air, piercing my ears and quickly sabotaging my short-lived peace. Loud footsteps thundered in the distance, rapidly closing in behind me!

Then I felt the sharp sting of a slap across my back and the pain of my hair being ripped from my scalp. Desperate, I glanced around in all directions hoping to find an avenue of escape before I became a helpless victim again!

Looking frantically to the right of the balcony, I saw a burning rope swinging from a tree.

To the left, I saw another rope swinging from another tree — but this rope was not on fire!

Afraid of heights, I was reluctant to choose either rope, but the screams were growing louder and closer, and the force that held me by the hair of my head was beginning to tow me back into the house!

I had to choose an escape route quickly, but which swinging rope should I pick?

Struggling free from the force, I ran to the right side of the balcony to the burning rope because it appeared to be closer. Peering over the edge, I could not believe the putrid sight!!! At the bottom of the burning rope was a huge blazing fire, and to my bewilderment, there were hundreds of people standing in the midst of the burning blaze!

Although their bodies were merely reduced to incandescent corpses, through the blazes they reached up to me moaning and groaning lyrical chants of the dead and forsaken! Begging me to join them, they wildly danced among the flames as if they were flirting with Satan's wrath!

While their bodies were grossly distorted, savagely singed and brutally burned by the fire, I squeamishly recognized some of the tarnished faces. These faces, faces I had not seen in years, were faces of people who had hurt me, faces I had banished from my memories many years ago.

Trying to elude the fire and the burning bodies, I stumbled to the other side of the balcony and reached out to the other rope. At this point, it mattered not to me what might lay at the bottom because it did not seem possible that it could be worse than the true Hell waiting at the end of the first rope.

So I stretched and reached out for the second rope as far as I could, yet I was unable to touch it. Glancing at the ground below, trying to estimate the distance if I should fall, I noticed that there, too, were hundreds of people. But unlike the first group, these people were all dressed in white, humming a melodious tune and calling out my name sweetly while coaxing me to jump towards their rope!

I plunged over the balcony rail, desperately grabbing for the rope.

"Even if I fall and die," I thought, "at least I will not burn in Hell with the ghosts of my past!"

As I started to descend through the air, I felt the sinewy rope within the palms of my hands. Clutching it firmly, the rope suddenly began to swing violently, as if it were trying to shake me off! And even my solid grasp could not hang on to the frenetically jerking rope. I started slipping down its fibrous trail.

Quickly, I looked towards the ground once again, and mysteriously, the angelic people in white were being ravaged by a raging fire, burning as grotesquely as the first group of harrowing, burning people from my past!

The crackling of the roaring fire deafened my ears.

The smell of burning flesh turned my stomach.

And the sounds of their frantic screams tortured me.

"Die, Leah, die! You have sinned! Burn! Burn in Hell! Burn in Hell forever like us! We've got you now, Leah! Just let go!"

My will caved in. I released the rope from my grasp. Tightly closing my eyes, I felt my body plummeting through the air, anticipating the stinging bite of the roaring flames!

But this descent into Hell did not occur as I had expected. I never reached the ground. Instead, I just kept falling and falling, gaining speed as I fell. Faster and faster I descended!

And once again, I felt stinging hands grasping at my breasts and flagellating my body!

Prying open my eyes, the twisted, dripping, burning faces lunged toward me screaming:

"You shouldn't have trusted the light! Never trust the light!"

Then the fire decided to unleash its fury upon me, molesting me with its penetrating blaze as if I were nothing but flammable fuel aiding its path of plundering. The fiery pillaging soon engulfed my entire body, and the pain was beyond compare. And to further mock my agony, the rigorous force was back — pushing my body and abandoned soul towards a burning bed in the corner of the bright, red room.

My hands were viciously pinned above my head, harshly tied to the bedposts. From the painful position in which I was lying, unable to budge, all I could see were the burning ceiling and the walls of the room. To deny the pain from the incessant and brutal molestation, I focused on a water spot on the ceiling of the red room and repeated the Lord's prayer again and again in my mind.

Then I screamed:

"Just take me! Kill me! I'm ready to die! Just release me from your grasp. Please! Please! Please!

"I'm sorry for my sins! I'm truly sorry!"

The water spot upon which I had been focusing started dripping.

Assuming that the dripping was merely a leakage of water or something, at first I felt a little twinge of hope, thinking God was saving me from the burning bed by sending water to put out the fire! Soon, the drips became a trickle, and the trickle became a stream. Then, the ceiling began to buckle from the weight of the immense pressure, and the walls began to crack. Suddenly, the ceiling gave way and the walls completely caved in!

I was saved! I was saved, I was saved!

But then why was the oppressive force still on top of me? I could hear its heavy breathing and terribly chilling, haunting laugh in my ears:

"You can't decline the Devil's invitation to dance, can you Leah? You can not resist his desire! For I am the devil and you are dwelling in my dungeon, now! Give in, Leah! Give in!"

With the immense water pressure pounding down from the ceiling and out of the walls all over my body, it was difficult to see anything.

But finally, I opened my eyes enough to behold my surroundings quite vividly. Horrified and shocked, I realized that the liquid that I had assumed to be water wasn't water at all — it was blood!

The entire room was overflowing with thick, red, disgusting blood! Blood was everywhere! Even the mattress and bed sheets were oozing with blood!

And strangely, the more blood that poured into the room showering my body, the greater the fire enveloping the bed burned me!

"Help! Help me!" I pleaded. "Someone, please help me!"

Out of nowhere, I heard a familiar voice call out my name.

"Leah, are you okay?"

It was the voice of my older sister, Lori.

"Please stop making so much noise and go to sleep, will you? I'm trying to sleep and there is no reason to be afraid of the dark."

As Lori's voice continued to coax me into silence, the debilitating force finally released me from its hold and dissipated into oblivion.

I could not believe the demon was gone! Gone too were the burning bed, bloody sheets and satanic room!

Bewilderingly, I found myself standing alone in my old bedroom of the trailer where I lived during my youth.

Even though the force was gone and I was at least in a familiar environment, I was still so frightened, I just wanted to feel safe. I wanted Lori to wrap her arms around me and hug me like she used to when we were kids and I was afraid.

Lori was always a very nurturing type and usually tried to comfort and protect me whenever she could, when she felt I truly needed it.

And at this particular moment, I desperately needed comforting and protecting!

"Is this a dream?" I asked myself. "Is this real? Why are Lori and I back in our old trailer? It was destroyed over 10 years ago! Is this really happening?"

Whatever the answers, I knew my older sister would protect me, if she could! I just had to get to her room and let her know I needed her help.

Her bedroom seemed a hundred miles away.

And after attempting unsuccessfully to beg her to come to my room, I assumed that she had become irritated by my incessant screams and had perhaps closed her door, keeping her from hearing my cries for help. So I dizzily made my way down the seemingly endless hall to her room. I was so petrified by the dark and afraid that the evilness would soon return, I had difficulty making myself take each step further and further into the darkness. But I finally reached Lori's door. Though I was tempted to bang on the door and rush into her room and arms for safety, I maintained my discipline and gently pushed it open so I wouldn't wake her if she were asleep. As I drew closer to her bed, I saw her figure under the covers and detected the rhythmic whispers of her breath.

"Wow," I thanked my lucky stars, "I must be safe and not dreaming anymore."

I was in Lori's room and everything seemed normal.

Her country music was playing softly in the background, and I could see the painted faces of the clowns that she collected lining the shelves and littering the walls. And Lori's soft, cushy carpet seemed to melt under my feet, and the scent of her perfume was lingering in the air.

I began to cry from relief. Collapsing at the foot of her bed, I delicately placed my wet face against the bed post. Soothed simply by knowing Lori was near, I felt safe and warm.

Sitting there in Lori's room in the dark, I tried to relive the strange and unbelievable occurrences of the night, but my mind was totally exhausted and unable to make sense out of anything. I grew so very sleepy that I concluded everything certainly had been a very, very scary and life-like nightmare.

Nestling closer to Lori for warmth and comfort, I suppose I awakened her.

Lori sprang straight up in bed and glared at me wickedly. I immediately assumed she must have been mad at me for interrupting her sleep. I quickly tried to explain what was going on and why I was in her room:

"The Devil was here tonight after me!" I cried. "The Devil was here! Help me, Lori! Please help me be rid of him!"

Lori slowly turned her head towards me and fiendishly grinned.

She was wearing the mask of one of her clowns.

Her eyes flashed and turned a fiery red as she opened her mouth to speak. And the voice that pierced my ears was not the voice of my sister. Instead, an evil, sinister and intensely loud voice boomed out:

"You silly fool! The Devil was here, huh? So, you think that the Devil was here? Well, I have news for you. The Devil is still here because I am the Devil! I am the Devil! As I told you before, you can not elude my embrace! Dance with me, Leah! Dance! Take my hand and dance!"

Horrified, I screamed at the night, trying to escape the blaze of her sinister glare.

"You are the Devil! You are the Devil! You are the Devil!" I repeatedly yelled.

"God, please save me! I do not want to dance with the Devil! God, please help me!"

Chapter Three

Walking in the Shoes of Bulimia

I suddenly awoke to cold water splashing me in the face and found myself buried in the strong arms of a friend trying to stop my frantic kicking and screaming.

I had been yelling the words "You are the Devil!" again and again so loudly that I had awakened my friend and her husband where I was staying.

For hours until dawn, they comforted and repeatedly assured me that everything would be fine. But even as the morning sunlight streamed in the window, I was still spooked and unable to go back sleep.

Although I recognized that the past night had all truly been just a bad nightmare, I knew there were many truths and unspoken meanings within the events of the dream. For hours until dinner, I stayed in the bedroom, pondering the demented truths and real meanings, several of which I had never consciously known before.

Unexpectedly, the wicked nightmare had unleashed the prison doors in my mind, releasing its hostile and heinous prisoners upon me with their built-up years of fury. These captives of my unconsciousness, these guilty culprits from my Hell, these demons of my past were now free to invade my daily awareness and existence.

Temporarily locked up again by the day's light, I knew they truly existed and where to find them. But I wasn't ready to confront them, especially not alone.

Unsuccessfully, I had tried to deal with one of the demons before, only to fail miserably and to find myself the victim of my own self-hatred and punishment. And as a result of my failure to cope with the brutal reality of the abuse of body as a child, not to mention later acts of abuse, I had spent the majority of my entire life compulsively overeating.

Does that make common sense?

No.

But that's what I did.

I foolishly attempted to bury my secrets away with the vast amounts of food I ritually consumed only to purge them from my body, incessantly, in an attempt to cleanse the food and the demons from my soul.

Therefore, it was a frightening awakening to realize that all my attempts to find peace, hide my shame and control my life had been in vain.

I now knew that to decapitate the Devil himself, as well as to destroy all his accompanying demons, I needed help — professional help.

For so long, I had been hiding from these wicked realities and ghosts of my past. I had thought that by tucking shameful memories away, back far in the dusty nooks and crannies of my mind, that I would never have to suffer from the nasty and unpleasant consequences of their memories again.

But too many factors had begun to surface in my life that contradicted this belief, the only too-real nightmare had been one.

If I were ever going to be content with myself, if I were ever going to successfully win my battle against bulimia, if I were ever going to make someone else happy, I knew that I could hide from my past no more.

The time had come to face my demons.

I don't remember exactly when or how I became so obsessed with food and how I looked.

For me, I've always hated myself, thus tried very hard to be perfect so at least other people would like me.

No matter what I've attempted in life, I've pressured myself to be perfect. Not average. Not good. Not mediocre. Only the very best.

I also incorrectly thought that by achieving popularity, fame and accomplishments, I would be validated as a good and worthy person.

And, putting all this together, I believe it was a combination of my drive for perfection, my denial of the past abuses, along with my quest for success and acceptance that created the "Bulimic Monster" I had become.

After living more than twelve years at the mercy of Bulimia and Anorexia Nervosa, I waited until my diseases became life-threatening before I sought medical help and finally admitted to having a food addiction — as well an addiction to needing to be loved.

Through the therapy I've received so far, as well as turning my life over to the care of my God, I've been able to see myself and my problems more clearly.

I realize that like all creatures, I am truly a precious child of God, someone worthy as a person and someone who deserves to be loved. And I have learned to begin forgiving myself for the "crimes" of my past — some I had control over, many I did not.

I have begun cleansing my soul of the years of anger and hatred. I have begun loving myself, accepting my personal progress without requiring perfection. And as I begin to accept myself as myself, I am learning how to more freely give and share my love with others.

For the first time since I was twelve years old, I feel as if I am alive and actually participating in life, as opposed to being obsessed and trapped by my addictions and merely "existing" until the next binge or "mission of perfection" to accomplish.

I am by no means cured. I still have mountains to climb — but I also know I now have wonderful islands to explore, too, happy places I never before knew even existed in this life.

But of course, it takes years to physically recover from extreme cases of Bulimia like mine. And in reality, no one is ever actually "cured" or free from the clutches of this disease. But I am trying very hard to face the abuses in my past, as well as life's simple misfortunes, with a new-found strength and hope from God that I am learning to control and live with my disease, one day at a time.

Every person suffering from this disease suffers for various reasons and in different ways and degrees.

I suppose you could define Bulimia in a hundred diverse ways.

For me, Bulimia is an eating disorder that resulted from my incredibly low self-esteem, as well as long periods of time that I deprived myself of food, hence my twin disease of Anorexia Nervosa, in which I would starve myself for days and weeks.

When I was younger, I was overweight. At that time, I deprived myself of food because I detested being ridiculed, and weight was the one thing in my youth that I could control! As time passed, I also grew to associate being overweight — food — as being "bad."

Combined with the notion that I was fat, ugly, and unworthy, my worst bout with anorexia caused me to starve down to about 98 pounds.

There wasn't much of me except bones.

Chapter Four

War to End All Wars

After joining the U.S. Army ROTC program in college in 1986, I simply could not physically compete with my peers at a feebly low and unhealthy weight.

Serving my country in the Army meant more to me than anything else in the entire world. And as an army officer, it was my responsibility to set the example, and that meant I had to eat if I was to be an efficient leader and to uphold the standards required of me.

So, when I "allowed" myself permission to eat again, at least temporarily, I absolutely thought I was in Heaven!

It had been a very long time since I had experienced the pleasure of eating. But, as always, the food was soon followed by the feelings of "badness" associated with eating, plummeting my low self-esteem even lower.

Nonetheless, I was powerless to resist the temptation of food, so I ate and I ate and ate! I had become a certifiable food addict. But I could not fathom this concept, nor could anyone else around me. Therefore, overcome with guilt and remorse after eating anything at all, I had to live out my reactive responses to the food in secret.

I reasoned that if I still thought my gluttonous overeating was simply a lack of willpower, then no one else would understand that I was suffering from a disease either. Thus, after constantly surrendering to the paramount temptation of eating, I felt weak and "bad," but I had to conceal my self-anger from others in fear that my secret might be discovered.

And all the secrecy surrounding my disease, as well as all the lies I had to tell in order to prevent its detection, intensified my derangement and depression while simultaneously increasing my detestation for food and myself even more!

It didn't take me long to rediscover my old technique that satisfied both my yearning for food, as well as my need to be thin. I began purging my food immediately after eating, then continued the purge through compulsive and excessive exercising. These processes allowed me the "wicked luxury" of tasting food — and what a delicacy that was — but not of suffering the consequences of feeling "bad" and fat.

Soon, I started eating more and more, virtually non-stop. Instead of eating one bowl of cereal in the morning, I would eat the entire box! It was such a delight to actually eat, I just couldn't refrain and control myself. But the more I ate, the more time I spent in the bathroom getting sick and in the gym working out and running.

By the time I was forced to seek help, I had been a victim of this nasty habit on and off for 12 years, and my entire life had become unmanageable.

Even though I only remembered commencing this habit after joining ROTC in 1986, actually it was a reoccurrence of a familiar behavior I had begun in my early youth. Vomiting my food after eating had become such a normal part of my life, I had forgotten when I had actually first fallen at the feet of this embarrassing, destructive disease. In fact, it had become such a normal part of my everyday life, I even accepted my behavior as right-minded. And since no one ever noticed my behavior, or at least no one ever confronted me, I reasoned that it couldn't be that bad.

Being totally obsessed with food is like being head-over-heels in love. No matter how much you try to work, play, sleep, relax, whatever, your mind is completely absorbed in thoughts of that special person.

Of course my love was food, followed closely by purging.

When I was at work, I had to make myself stay busy in order not to eat. When I was talking to a friend, I tried to listen to the conversation, but usually thoughts of food were flying around in my mind. I would even get up in the middle of the night before I was conscious and shove tons of food down my throat! Food was the first thing I thought of each morning as I awoke, and it was the last thing I thought of before going to bed.

When company visited, I was simply waiting for them to leave so I could rush to the refrigerator. My friends no longer called to ask me out, because I always refused in order to be alone with my food and the toilet. I had absolutely no attention span, because I was either planning what I was going to eat next and how I was going to sneak it, or I was punishing myself for having done just that.

Thoughts of food controlled my life, my actions, and my moods — and even my relationships. I never experienced a single day of sanity. After depriving my body of food for so long, my body actually physically craved food. In fact, my body and my mind craved food so much that the taste of food and the actual feeling of food in my mouth, going down my throat into my stomach, felt like ecstasy! I couldn't stop eating because the sensation was too great!

Food! Food! Food! Glorious food!

I found myself completely out of control and passionately participating in the pathetic art of ravenous bingeing. Yet, since I would feel guilty after eating even a morsel, I absolutely despised myself after bingeing for hours. I would feel obese, disgusting, like the scum of the earth.

I could already see the fat sticking to my thighs only seconds after eating anything, at all!

How could I stand to "vomit" all day?

For some reason, I never really thought about "purging" and "vomiting" as being synonymous. "Purging" simply allowed me the pleasure of eating food without having to suffer the consequences of feeling fat.

Looking back, it's amazing how powerful the mind is. I thought I had only become unmanageably "sick" after winning the titles of Miss Tennessee in the Miss America 1992 contest and then Miss Tennessee in the Miss USA contest 1994. Granted, the additional pressures of pageantry to appear perfect and to be ideally thin further provoked my disease. But I simply had not realized the seriousness of my problem prior to my "pageant life" — nor actually really admitted that I even had a problem — because vomiting had become a normal escape for me.

I didn't understand why I continued to binge and purge, until it was almost too late.

Through therapy, I've had to bring painful memories to the surface which I had long ago tucked away. Many people still mistakenly attribute my Bulimia to my involvement in pageants, my starvation for attention and my natural desire to always be in the limelight. Admittedly, being a perfectionist, as well as being in the limelight, created additional incentives to look nice, yet my entire involvement in pageants was actually a product of my low self-esteem, not vice versa.

My interest in beauty pageants derived from a need to be accepted by society. I wanted the world to think I was pretty. I wanted to use my intelligence and the forum of being a beauty queen to make a difference in the world. I pretended that I was, indeed, that beautiful, powerful horse in my land of make-believe that everyone noticed and everyone admired. I simply needed to be loved and accepted. Can that be too hard to understand? I thought that if I could win the title of Miss America or Miss USA, I would also win society's approval that "Leah Hulan is okay!"

I needed, or at least I thought that I needed, everyone to admire me in order for me to feel good about myself.

All my life I had been abused mentally, physically, and sexually. The ugliness and humiliation of these acts against me deteriorated my confidence and self-esteem, causing my loathsome self-disgust and unacceptance. Because I hated myself so very much, I needed everyone else to adore me! It was extremely arduous for me to say "no" to anyone about almost anything, afraid that I might be rejected again. I just wanted to be loved and accepted. I just wanted to feel important.

Now, throughout my journey of self-discovery, I'm beginning to learn that Leah Hulan is not merely about her body — Leah Hulan is a kind, loving and gentle soul and is blessed with much more than an exterior, superficial frame.

But I didn't know that for a long, long time.

In my ongoing battle against Bulimia, I've learned that more people suffer from this disease than I could ever imagine. Perhaps everyone suffering from its vicious clutch does not suffer to the extent that I have, and certainly there are those who suffer even more. Yet, the numbers are astonishing and reveal that many victims of low self-esteem and sexual abuse result in the consequential suffering of an eating disorder, as well. And just like any other disease such as cancer or heart disease, willpower alone can not fight and cure the sickness. Eating disorders require professional attention, and there is help to be found.

Bulimia, and other eating disorders as well, can be controlled - but the ones who are suffering must be willing to fight and to surrender their "control" and willfulness to a Higher Power. For me, although I had never been a constantly devout and practicing Christian, I had a strong faith in religion and perceived my Higher Power to be God. However, I have many friends in treatment who are atheists, yet still surrendered their control to a power they felt was greater than themselves. For many of them, their Higher Power simply was the "power" of a support group or family members and friends. One of my friends even found her "higher power" through the strength she found within her adoration of nature and music.

Ironically, by giving up "control" of my life, I actually gained a more profound power. Armed with God by my side, I no longer was ill-prepared to battle my belligerent Bulimarexia nor to decapitate my old demons. And fortunately for me, what a salvation! For fighting the malicious malady plaguing my body and mind was like no struggle that I had ever encountered before. I had no idea the battle would be so complex nor so difficult and would forever be an enemy with which I would have to contend.

I had always prided myself in my strength and thought I was prepared to surmount almost any obstacle thrown in my path. I mean, I had not only served in the United States Army through one invasion in Central America, but I also had served during the Desert Storm War.

I thought that after overcoming these life-threatening events, I could easily overcome anything!!!

Wrong!

My battle against Bulimia has been an on-going battle since its inception. Even though I feel like I'm working a strong and solid program of recovery, there have been some gloomy days when I've lost precious and hard-fought ground to my seemingly omnipotent foe once again. Yet, I've found that only through my mistakes do I seem to learn, and with renewed determination, I'm then able to progress forward through the solidly entrenched enemy lines. Often I enjoy the serenity of weeks without a single compulsive confrontation. But when I least expect it, my antagonistic adversary will launch a new offensive empowered with the traditional "element of surprise" as its weapon of destruction.

As a consequence, I'm forced to counter-attack through prayer and through my strict adherence to the principles of my 12 Step program. This particular program has consistently supplied me with endless reserves of "ammunition" and successful "wartime tactics" that even during my weakest moments in battle, enabled me to outmaneuver or overpower my dangerous disease again.

And another part of the "winning tactics" that I employ is the support of fresh, well-trained, battle "reinforcements." These reinforcements consist of a rather diverse, but most efficient group of professional combatants — my family, my close friends, my fellow peers in recovery, the support groups from my treatment centers, and my various counselors and therapists. They serve as my "aides de camp," my "search and rescue" team, my "demolition" team, as well as special envoys and wartime advisers.

All I have to do is call upon them to tap into their unwavering determination to help me win this, my "war to end all wars."

Chapter Five

Point of No Return

While I had experienced many frightening nightmares before the burning ropes, that marked my point of no return.

With that dream, the reality of the past had surfaced in the nightmare's horrors. I was not prepared to deal with these truths, yet I didn't know where to hide them anymore, leaving me more ashamed and more stressed than ever.

My safe, little world was quickly closing in on me. I knew that I needed to seek professional help, and I had tried several times. But it seemed every time I reached out for help, I was humiliated. I had no money and no insurance.

Overcome with depression in addition to my sickness, nothing seemed simple or clear. I felt as if I were drifting around aimlessly in nonexistence. Living was providing me no purpose for my torturous existence, and I had no energy or motivation to even get out of bed. I slept many days away, and when I wasn't sleeping, I was sobbing myself into oblivion. The tears just kept flowing and flowing, and I did not understand why.

One morning, I decided to call my mom for some encouragement to help me out of the dark depths where I had fallen, but there was no answer. I then tried to call my sister, but again, there was no answer.

I got out of bed and looked into the mirror. What a pitiful and fat image I beheld in the reflection. So in order to make myself feel better and worthy of living, I pulled my jogging clothes and shoes out of the closet and motivated myself for a 10-mile run. Anything less than 10 miles certainly would not suffice in restoring my ability to feel good that day, and I felt I had no choice but to run the entire distance at once. But after only running six and a half miles, I simply did not have anymore energy to complete the course.

Collapsing at my driveway after dragging my feet and stumbling the rest of the way home, I felt like a total failure, as usual. What was three and a half more miles? I could not understand why my body was not reacting properly, in accordance with the demands of my mind. Instead of praising my blistered feet for a solid run at greater than average speed, I ignored the accomplishment and with renewed energy marched straight to the refrigerator.

There wasn't a lot of tasty or healthy food in the refrigerator or pantry to choose from, but without consciously thinking, I began to eat everything my hungry eyes fell upon.

First, I ate the rest of the spaghetti left over from three days before. It was cold and not very appetizing, but the noodles were greasy and slid down my throat easily. Still feeling famished, I ate a huge Tupperware bowl of cereal, using all the milk. After wolfing down the first bowl too fast to even taste it, I opened a family size box of Honey Nut Cheerios and emptied its entire contents into a large casserole dish so I could indulge myself in ecstasy for at least a few minutes or so!

Momentarily upset, remembering that I had already consumed all the milk in the house, I decided to saturate my "cereal casserole" with water. Reasoning that skim milk was almost eighty percent water anyway, I rationalized that plain tap water would taste the same as the dairy substitute! Grasping my huge dish with both hands, I lifted my delicacy to the sink and ran cold water straight from the faucet onto the heaping concoction. And after tossing about ten packets of Equal on top of my massive entree, I animalistically devoured the entire dish in a matter of minutes, barely taking time to swallow or breathe.

Leaning back from my feast, I was physically miserable and mentally furious at myself after eating such a magnanimous amount, so I jumped up and ran up and down the hall to shake up the food in my stomach.

And just seconds later, I experienced utter relief and a delightful high as I unsteadily loomed over the toilet, bowed my head and vomited for a good 15 minutes. Disgusting as it was, discharging all the food seemed nearly as challenging and rewarding as liberating Kuwait from Iraq! But what an undignified triumph about which to boast, even though I was actually proud to have ridded myself of most of the "toxin" on the first try!

Nonetheless, my temporary outburst of pride soon dispersed, along with my purge-induced, euphoric high. And as this sensation evaporated into mere agitation, I was left high and dry, alone in my befuddlement.

Not only had I blown my diet for the day and failed to complete my little run, but also my sudden dissension from my high lapsed me even further into an inescapable depression.

What to do?

I headed straight back to the refrigerator.

I ate pickles, crackers and mustard, eggs and cheese, everything I could find! Then I began craving something sweet, but all I could find was a chocolate cake mix in the cabinet. I decided if I cooked it quickly, I could eat it all without anyone knowing it! The instructions on the back of the box stated it would take about 45 minutes to bake, but I couldn't wait that long. Instead, I mixed the contents up in a bowl and placed it in the microwave to cook for about 10 minutes while I occupied myself with some macaroni and cheese. Although the cake wasn't exactly pretty enough for a party, I certainly feasted well! The texture was more like that of a huge brownie rather than a cake, but I engulfed the entire thing without a fuss. It was fabulously divine! Until, of course, I began to get full again and was ready to purge.

Feeling nauseated by the bizarre mix of foods I had so quickly consumed, vomiting was effortless this time — like the good old days before I developed bleeding throat ulcers and esophagus cramps!

But, of course, the sadistic cycle reared its ugly power.

Coming back to reality out of my "Food Fix" like a crack addict withdrawing from drugs, I sat down on the floor and cried.

"Leah, you are so, so very sick! You are disgusting! What is wrong with you? Why can't you stop this foolishness? It hurts you so much, why can't you stop?"

My throat was aching and bleeding because the potent acids in my stomach as I regurgitated repetitively burned the open sores ever present on its inner walls. My throat had already been raw and inflamed and almost swollen shut from all the continuous vomiting over the last several months anyway. I held my head in my hands and pulled my tangled mess of hair while screaming in confusion and in desperation.

"Someone help me! Someone help!"

There was no answer.

I had to escape. I just had to get away! But where could I go to evade the pain that I was feeling inside my mind? I would never be able to get away from myself! I had tried. God, how I had tried! Now, I was desperate. I would do anything to be free of the burdens which haunted me! I just wanted to be free of the pain!

At that very moment, I wanted to die.

When I heard myself ask God to grant me the gift of death, my unconscious fighting spirit knew it was past time to give up or to act.

I crawled to my bedroom and found the telephone book under the bed. Bawling my eyes out, I dialed a number advertising counseling for "psycho-somatic eating disorders." It was all I could do just to have the strength to make the call for help.

An unsympathetic voice answered. My voice quivering, I asked for the extension for the Eating Disorders unit.

"We don't have any eating disorder programs available at this time," she snapped.

"Click."

She hung up on me without a pause.

I yelled out loud to no one:

"Can you believe that? She hung up on me! Here I am, desperate for help, clinging to what little sanity I have left, and when I call a hospital for help, a nurse hangs up on a crying person!"

Shaking with fury, I voraciously searched through the yellow pages, furiously dialing all the numbers advertising programs for eating disorders. Once I admitted I had no medical insurance, not one single place gave me the time of day.

At wit's end, I dialed a suicide hot line. The man sort of laughed when I described my problem.

I was about to lose it! I felt myself edging closer and closer to falling off the wall of sanity into the world of lunacy. I was dizzy. I was depressed. I was ashamed and embarrassed. And now I was humiliated, too.

Staring blankly at the meaningless telephone numbers, I felt my mind escape my body, floating up into the space above and then looking down upon me from the ceiling.

I saw a pitiful little girl, all curled up in a fragmented mess, sobbing on the floor. Her long blonde hair was pasted to her face and stuck to her neck, wet from tears and vomiting. Her once sparkling blue eyes were bloodshot and nearly swollen together. And her bony hands trembled as they weakly grasped her knobby knees close to her heaving chest as she rocked herself tenderly, back and forth, for comfort. As I looked closely at myself and perceived me as I truly was at that moment, I sadly asked:

"Who could love that girl? Just look at her now. No one deserves to suffer with her problems as she is suffering now. Especially her fiance, Tom, not him. He doesn't even know she has a problem! He's been stationed overseas for the past four years! He could never understand. God, I'm glad he can't see her now! He would really be ashamed to have her as a fiancee!"

As my mind descended back down from its lofty perch and drifted back into my body, I slept.

Chapter Six

Self Sabotage

I awoke from a deep sleep hours later to the sound of the phone ringing.

I don't actually even remember the call or even with whom I spoke. Yet, after the call, I felt calm and determined, determined to get well — but without letting the entire world know about my sickness!

I mean, if the media caught wind that Miss Tennessee USA™ 1994 was puking her guts up everyday while giving speeches about "believing in yourself," what would happen then, to me and the pageant system I respected?

So, acting impulsively and being over-anxious to start solving my problems at once, I made what may have been one of the most regrettable mistakes in my life. I picked up the phone, called Tom and sabotaged our happiness and possible future together.

I canceled our wedding and engagement.

I was alone a few days later when I was medically diagnosed as having acute Bulimia and as suffering from severe depression. It was recommended that I become an in-patient immediately at a hospital or institution specializing in eating disorders. But first, I had to undergo a full physical examination to determine the extent of damage my twelve years of regurgitation had caused my body.

Some of the problems that were found were problems I had already been aware of for years, such as bleeding ulcers, esophagus cramps, impaired vision and an inability to get warm. For example, for at least five years, I have been cold to the bone. It could be 80 degrees in the house, and I would still have to wear sweat pants, a sweater and wool socks just to stay warm. And, working full-time at the National Guard Armory, I was very uncomfortable because we had to keep the temperatures low to protect the sensitive equipment and computers. I often had to wear my field jacket or sweater inside the buildings, even in the summertime, or have to go outside in the sun to "thaw" every hour. Little did I know that this phenomenon was a result of my Bulimia. All along, I had thought that my body simply hadn't acclimatized to the cooler temperatures of North America after being stationed in the army in Central America.

What wonders a sick mind can drum up!

Although I had been aware of many symptoms of my disease, I was shocked by some of the other, more serious symptoms indicated by the test results, such as my liver deterioration and the development of an irregular heartbeat — the apparent cause for my self-named "mini heart attacks."

Several times during the last three years, I had experienced a sudden, excruciating pain in my chest that left me breathless, dizzy, and unable to move my arms for fifteen to twenty minutes. I coined the term "mini heart attack" in reference to the sensation, because prior to the bolt of pain ripping through my chest, my heart would begin to race uncontrollably.

One time was especially etched in my mind.

I was participating in a joint National Guard mission in Hawaii with Hawaii's Marijuana Eradication Team. That day, I was up in an intelligence gathering helicopter attempting to locate harvests of illegally grown marijuana when one of these "mini heart attacks" besieged me. Trying to conceal the sudden attack and control the pain while continuing the mission was not an easy feat. I was also afraid the chopper's constant and swift changes in altitude would provoke my heart to prolong its rapid beating. Luckily, I was firmly belted into my seat because when the attack unexpectedly occurred, I lost all voluntary movement in my entire upper body. My arms and neck were actually immobile and useless, and I feared I was paralyzed. I panicked and wanted desperately to cry for help and to command the civilian pilot to ground the helicopter. But I didn't. I just slumped back into the confines of my safety harness and tried to focus my undivided attention on spotting marijuana. By the time the pilot landed to refuel two hours later, I felt almost normal again, relieved from concern — until the next bizarre attack.

Other damage that the constant purging had caused me physiologically included menstrual irregularity, constipation, fatigue, weakness, hair loss, generalized swelling and salivary gland irritation. Although none of these signs were life threatening, the conditions were indications that more serious damage was occurring. Just for example, right before I competed in the Miss USA pageant in February 1994, I completely lost my voice and was vomiting blood. No one knew the real reason why I had lost my voice, except me. The constant purging had caused my esophagus to repetitively tear and form scar tissue all along my throat. And as I starved down to below 100 pounds just prior to competing in Miss USA by steadily vomiting without eating, the only substances that I could purge became the potent digestive acids and green bile from my intestines. These acids severely burned the pre-existing scar tissue lining my throat and formed new ulcers on top of already inflamed, bleeding sores.

So, even though I appeared healthy on the outside, the inside of my body was very ill and very malnourished. As a result, I had become prone to kidney and bladder infections, as well as causing a possible "shut-down" of my entire digestive system.

My metabolism was barely functioning because my body was either starving for days or was suddenly overwhelmed with gargantuan amounts of food. Also, my back was constantly in pain, walking was often difficult, and urination was severely discomforting. And to make matters worse, my blood sugar levels were abnormal and my doctors had temporarily feared diabetes. Luckily, after receiving treatment, my blood sugar levels stabilized. However, I still suffer from the fear of permanent damage done to my eyes and to my female organs.

Due to the strain of frequent and intense vomiting, my eyesight has rapidly decreased to near legal blindness. Without wearing my contacts or glasses, I cannot see well enough to walk up a flight of stairs.

And, as far as the permanent damage done to my reproductive system, I'm still waiting to find out. I have not had a regular menstrual cycle in over nine years. Even with the use of medically prescribed hormones, there has been no change in my condition, so the possibility exists that I will never be able to bear children.

The doctors prescribed a drug called Prozac which supposedly works almost like a "miracle drug" in treating depression and, consequently, Bulimia. But after filling the prescription, I was actually scared and reluctant to use the drug, even as prescribed by my trusted doctor. The reason was that I was preparing to accompany my National Guard unit to South America for annual training, and I simply didn't want to be under the influence of a new drug.

And to be squarely honest, I had also fooled myself into irrationally thinking that I could beat this problem without the aid of any medication. That seems almost silly now, but at that particular time in my addiction, I really needed to feel that I could control at least one thing in my life. I was still denying how serious my problem had become, even though my therapist was adamant about my needing the medication, as well as seeking in-patient treatment. He firmly believed that my degree of suffering could only be alleviated with professional help and definitely in a controlled environment. Nonetheless, my Prozac remained untouched in its little container on the shelf of my bathroom.

Only months later, when my illness became so severely life threatening that I felt that I had no other alternative but to try the drug did I retrieve the medicine from its nearly forgotten shelf.

Unfortunately, I did not take the Prozac steadily as prescribed. Instead, I often doubled the dosages, depending on my degree of depression at that particular moment.

I would use the drug on and off until this innocent, but mismanaged abuse, nearly killed me on 19 October, 1994.

Chapter Seven

Silent Screams

With the help of professional treatment, I have realized that my Bulimia is a product of my impaired sense of self-worth and self-confidence.

Before I began my recovery, I constantly compared myself with others and always saw myself as less attractive, less capable and less interesting. I tried to over-compensate by achieving nothing less than perfection, thinking that if I accomplished everything perfectly, then I could escape my innate fear of any possible criticism from others. Consequently, I've often read that Bulimics are neither able to recognize their own successes nor accept the recognition of their successes by others. That certainly described me rather accurately!

I used to think that no amount of attention, no amount of love, and no amount of success was ever going to be good enough for me because I always wanted more and more!

I assumed a false identity of the happy, strong "Leah" that I wanted to be. I adorned myself with many smiling masks, always afraid that someone might see the shame and sin smeared all over my true face.

This obsessive quest of mine to constantly achieve greater and greater popularity, success, and accomplishments, at the expense of my own happiness, had left me unable to fully appreciate many of the goals that I had already accomplished.

After graduating fourth out of a high school class of 400, I felt that I must not have been very smart after all because my goal had been to graduate as the Valedictorian. Also, to me, earning the second highest rank in college ROTC was a failure because I had competed for the Battalion Commander position, not the Executive Officer. Likewise, although earning a Regular Army commission in the United States Army Military Intelligence was the greatest moment in my life, I sacrificed that honor for an appointment in the National Guard so I could attempt my luck in pageants! Consequently, winning the title of Miss Tennessee 1992 was a short-lived success, even though Tennessee's pageant was one of the most sought after crowns because it offered more scholarship money than any other state contest at the time.

For some reason, I thought that if I could win another title, then I would be a good, worthy, and beautiful person once again, who was also living up to the high expectations that I had unknowingly placed upon myself. So I tried one last time to be a winner in the other pageant system and surprisingly won the coveted title of Miss Tennessee USA 1994. Seldom in history had anyone won two different state titles back to back, and this rarity enabled me to be one of the few young ladies in America to be able to compete in both The Miss America Pageant and The Miss USA Pageant.

Sadly, I nearly died before I realized all the wonderful opportunities and rare blessings that God had lavished upon me.

Not that I didn't try.

After my night of endless phone calls to treatment centers, I continued to try to get into others. In the meantime, I reluctantly settled for hourly sessions with a local psychologist, all I could afford.

In the aftermath of my meetings with my psychologist, I was always irritable and seriously upset. I rationalized that the therapy must not be working since my suppressed anger had caused me to binge after each appointment.

So, against my family's will, I decided to quit seeing the psychologist. But by this time, my family had acquired some general knowledge of Bulimia's health risks and was trying to help me abstain from overeating and then purging. But try as they might, they simply could not understand how this problem developed, why I could not control it, or why I would become enraged at them when they attempted to prevent me from eating all that I wanted. Also, even though they were concerned that I was afflicted with a disease, they still had no idea how impaired I had become. Their ignorance stemmed in part from my own ingenuity.

In order to conceal my food addiction and the physical symptoms of Bulimia from others, I had become a rather skilled liar or "actress," as I preferred to call it. So it was hardly my family's fault not to know that some of my organs had malfunctioned or that I was harboring many personal demons that were feeding my addictions. That's why they were trying to put a "band-aid" on my problem, as opposed to helping me deal with the real underlying issues causing my dementia. However, several times I had indeed risked revealing these "issues" to them, but my family was more in denial than I was.

In fact, over two years ago I actually sat my mother down and blatantly told her all about my food obsession. But, in time she seemed to have dismissed the conversation as another one of my ploys for attention. And during a festive night on the town, my older sister and I had an argument at a local restaurant. I apologized by standing up at the head of the table, admitting to being Bilimic and then explaining that this evil disease had been the real cause of the tension between us.

But after these two direct confessions and pleas for help, no one ever mentioned or even acknowledged that my problem was real.

I bitterly wondered if they were blind. My disease made me angry at them for not understanding. I mean, they had to notice the obvious indications, I reasoned!

Not only did I lose and gain weight rather often, but also I spent the majority of my time in the bathroom! During and after every meal, I would excuse myself to leave at least two to three times. When I would return to the table after a few minutes, my nose would be running and my eyes would be watering and red, yet no one seemed to notice! And after I had been home alone, all the food had mysteriously disappeared!

But there were times when I thought that my family might finally hear my silent — and sometimes not so silent screams.

On occasion, my mom would turn around from whatever she was doing and catch me vomiting in the yard, in the toilet, in the trash can, or really anywhere that was close. But instead of scolding me or even asking if I was all right, she would just go on like it was normal for her daughter to "puke" every hour!

I can't blame her. It was normal, for me anyway.

Now that my disease and all its accompanying symptoms are no longer a secret, my family have removed their "blinders" and have been an integral part in my recovery. My being rigorously honest with them, as well as with myself, has been a precious tool in my growing and healing process. Even though they hope that I'm on the road to complete recovery and maintaining my abstinence from bingeing and purging, it will be a battle that I will have to consciously fight each day for the rest of my life.

Someday, I hope that I can appreciate my life and see myself like my dearest friend, Sergeant Dan McCraw, sees me.

Always encouraging me and telling me that I am the most powerful person he knows, in his last letter from Korea, he wrote:

"Leah, I wish you could see yourself as the rest of the world sees you. You are always smiling and your smile brightens up an entire room! How many girls would die to trade places with you and be a Miss Tennessee twice!

"Not to be mean, Leah, but you have a lot to be thankful for. You are blessed with a great family, especially your grandmother! You live with her on and off and sacrifice much of your own life helping to take care of her as she herself combats cancer. And your personality, people just migrate to you. You can do anything in life that you want to, Leah!

"Just please, please stop taking these things and your health for granted! If you don't start helping yourself soon, you are going to die! Do you realize that Leah? You are going to die unless you get help. It is so important to me that you get this help now! You know I love you, don't you? But, you must begin to care about yourself! You can't keep running from this; it is very serious!

"Stop and think about the time you are taking off your life every time you throw up!

"Look, I supported you when you initially sought help. Then, I supported you when you received a little help. And now, I'll continue to support you as you still need more help! I realize you can't afford the treatment, but I will help you financially any way that I can. Even though I'm just an E-5, money is nothing compared to your life! The offer still exists, if you want. I'd do anything for you. I want you to get well!

"I just wish you knew how much you are truly loved by everyone that knows you!"

It was Dan's persistence and friendship that initially inspired me to seek help. He understood the enormity of the disease I was facing and its consequences more than I did. But of course he did. I was too far into my Bulimia and other addictions to see through the darkness enshrouding my existence.

Darkness.

It always seems to go back to that.

It makes sense that ever since I can remember, I have been afraid of the dark. Even today when I'm in my house, I'm over sensitive to lurking shadows and strange sounds when it's dark, especially when I'm alone.

"Alone." That is part of the darkness, the way I have always felt, alone.

Why did I feel that way?

My friend Dan and my therapist wholeheartedly agree that the answers to all my questions can only be found in confronting my past and finally ridding myself of the renegade rogues that have been hibernating in me far too long.

So, when did it all begin

Chapter Eight

April Fools

I was not conceived as a result of "love."

My parents had already separated and were contemplating divorce when a passionate night on my dad's houseboat produced another major antagonism to their rocky relationship — me.

Mom prayed and prayed that she had simply skipped her period due to stress or fatigue. But as fate would have it, her doctor confirmed her pregnancy. Today, Mom is thankful God chose not to answer her prayers. But at the time, she passionately prayed for her pregnancy to be terminated somehow. Realizing that a permanent reconciliation with my father was doubtful, and already having a 5-month-old infant to take care of, Mom seriously didn't think that she could afford to have another child under these circumstances. She wanted to be a good mother to the child she already had, and being able to provide her a healthy, loving environment was very important. She didn't want to sacrifice Lori's well-being for that of an unwanted, unneeded, and unborn child. Thus, she carefully considered her options, and having an abortion was one of them that was top on the list. The new life inside her was basically a mistake, and a costly one at that. If a divorce was eminent, Mom would soon be a single, unemployed mother returning to school for additional degrees. Having a second child would really be a heavy burden to bear alone.

Obviously, Mom opted to live with her mistake and make the best of a bad situation. I admire her for this difficult decision — especially under her then existing conditions — and am glad she allowed my life to continue. Even Mom recently confided in me that she, too, was glad for unanswered prayers.

"But, honestly," she told me. "If abortion had been legal, I probably would have had an abortion."

I was born into this world April 1, 1968, on the morning of April Fool's Day.

With my potent ability to pity myself, I've always thought I deserved to be born on the only day of the year that's a real joke.

Anyway, as predicted, my parents divorced soon after my birth.

I believe that moment to be the initial time loneliness and doubt began shadowing me, though I know it's widely debated as to when an infant's perceptions are truly created.

All I know is that I grew up feeling that there was something "bad" about me that caused my parents to stop loving each other. Whether I formed this opinion on my own, or if it were more attributable to the incessant teasing and taunting of my step-sisters as I grew up, who knows?

I just felt as if I had done something wrong to make Daddy go away.

While my mother is absolutely a brilliant person, it was partially due to her profound intelligence, wit and education that led to my parents tribulation. Although Daddy was exceptionally bright himself, I think he was a bit intimidated by my mother's powerful personality, as well as her degrees.

My father was 14 years older than my mother when they married, and although he was very intelligent, he did not have a college degree. In fact, due to World War II, my dad didn't even apply to college. Instead, he was drafted by Uncle Sam. Beyond the gap between their educational levels, being older, my father had rather solid ideas as to how a wife should behave.

My mother, on the other hand, had her own. And from the onset of their relationship, Mom and Dad shared differing opinions about almost everything else, as well.

But there was that initial attraction.

After the war ended, my father was hired at Arnold Engineering Development Center in Tullahoma, Tennessee. It was there that he met my mother, who was then a computer programmer. And when she laid eyes on my handsome, debonair father, she thought she fell in love.

Unfortunately though, instead of finding that real, tender, magical love that is so rare to touch upon, my parents had simply been in love with the idea of love. And caught up in their small society world, they succumbed to the pressures of the time and embellished in "appearances."

They were soon married, but trouble was already brewing.

Their extremely different personalities conflicted from the beginning. My Mom's personality was always in high gear. She absolutely loves life, always has a great time and truly enjoys talking to people. Born with a very inquisitive mind, she can figure out any puzzle, loves to travel and delights in trying new things. She's spontaneous, gregarious, humble and genuine.

In contrast, my dad was very private. Extremely conservative, he didn't enjoy large gatherings or parties. He was a workaholic. While he always made very smart decisions, it was only after long, calculated, hours of analysis that he would make them. Being a pure gentleman, he was charming, remarkably polite and a most loyal person.

He was simply a "listener." My mother was, without a doubt, a "talker."

I think my dad felt intimidated by Mom, because of her higher level of education, and because she made more money than he did. Whatever, they fell out of love with one another. They coexisted for awhile, barely tolerating each other, primarily for the sake of their infant child, Lori.

My unplanned birth was just too much.

Chapter Nine

Fly, Birdie, Fly!

From what I've heard, the divorce was not ugly.

Daddy willingly gave everything to my mother for the sake of his two daughters whom soon became his whole life. The only thing he was adamant about was visitation rights.

The courts allowed Daddy to have custody of us every other week-end.

To me, my father was the epitome of perfection, the ideal father. I always knew he adored me, even though I didn't get to see him as much as either of us wanted. It wasn't his fault that I felt abandoned by him, just because I didn't get to live with him.

Nonetheless, I did grow up feeling alone. I could never understand why he always had to say "good-bye." Why couldn't he tuck me in bed every night and kiss me gently on the forehead? Where was he when I cut my foot on the broken bottle? Or when Lori threw my Barbie out the window? Where was he to help me ride the tricycle he gave me or to read my story books to me when it was thundering and lightning outside? Who would protect me from the dark and check under the bed for monsters?

These are the questions that went unanswered during my very early youth. And even though I know now that Daddy always wanted to be at my side every second of the day, these unanswered questions were the seeds of my feelings of unworthiness.

Without my father on a daily basis, I quickly became my beloved granddaddy's "helper."

After the divorce, mom received a National Science Foundation Scholarship to attend a six week institute in Maryland, sending my sister and me to live with my grandparents.

Being about two years old, my grandfather quickly became my barrier against loneliness.

Granddaddy was a well-educated, hard-working man raised on a farm in Beechgrove, six miles down the road from the somewhat better known Bell Buckle, Tennessee. His mother died when he was still very young, so he took it upon himself to raise and educate his younger brother, as well as himself. They both attended Vanderbilt University, where he met my wonderful grandmother, whom we all call MaMay.

As a boy, he was quite a prankster. My favorite story is one about the thousands of beautiful, yellow buttercups planted along the Webb Highway on the way to Shelbyville. As the story goes, the schoolmaster at Granddaddy's high school administered "community service" as punishment for bad behavior. For each of his pranks, the schoolmaster ordered Granddaddy to clear a section of that roadside of all brush and debris and then to plant flowers.

To this day, I smile as I pass the miles and miles and miles of beautiful, dancing, yellow buttercups that my very own Granddaddy planted himself!

When we moved in with my grandparents, what fun Lori and I had! The farm was like a huge, unexplored amusement park that was open all day and all night, purely for our own entertainment and pleasure. We could never have been bored! There were animals and always more games to play, or a pond to explore, or a farmhand to pester! We especially enjoyed antagonizing Mrs. Lambert, MaMay's kindhearted maid who lived in the little red house on the farm. We would run around barefoot and almost "naked as blue jays," hair uncombed and climbing trees, possessing not a worry in the world and having the time of our lives!

Each day was a new adventure, and Granddaddy made these adventures more exciting than ever!

He used to pile Lori and me into the front seat of his old, blue pick-up truck and take us for a fast ride into Beechgrove. We'd wave at everyone in town, all twenty people, before stopping at "Miss Parker's Store." There, he'd buy us a big RC Cola and a chocolate moon pie. We'd sit outside on the porch with the other senior townsmen, whittling on old pieces of cedar, and listening attentively as they'd share their astonishing stories.

My grandfather's father was an alcoholic, and so was my Granddaddy, though I didn't know what that meant then.

All I knew was at times, he would disappear for days on a drunken stupor and return as if nothing had happened. I remember often hearing my grandparents argue at breakfast, though I hated hearing these heated conversations. Granddaddy would use many colorful words that I didn't understand. And when I would repeat them, especially the time I hollered a couple of my favorite ones out in church, I would get a big spanking!

I realize now it was his own disease of alcoholism that caused the tension between my grandparents and that ignited these routine quarrels. His alcoholism, like my Bulimia, manipulated his judgment, his moods and his actions. Even though he could often resist alcohol for months at a time, the disease still had a bad way of tarnishing and controlling his life.

But all I knew back then was that Granddaddy always had a bottle of "something" that he carried around in a little, red velvet bag with a shiny, gold drawstring. He said these bottles were full of "magic water," and that when he drank it, he became a stronger person. I imagined that his "magic water" was like Popeye's "magic spinach." He used to put a little bit on my thumb and let me taste it.

"Yuck!" I thought, since I didn't like it any better than I liked spinach!

"Wonder why all my heroes eat and drink such terrible stuff?"

Granddaddy loved to hunt for quail and doves, and I loved to tag along. I watched as his well-trained dogs consistently retrieved the birds without tearing them up. Then, Granddaddy would take each little bird in his hands and snap off its head, ever so easily.

I thought this was an especially fascinating maneuver, so I implored him to teach me his skillful craft. After attempting unsuccessfully for several minutes to snap off a quail head, I became bored with trying, and thought it would be more amusing to watch the bird fly again.

I tossed the limp bird into the air and yelled:

"Fly! Birdie! Fly!"

Of course the bird didn't fly at all. Instead, it came crashing down beside Granddaddy's feet. I started to cry because I thought I had hurt the bird.

"Granddaddy, I hurt the little birdie! He won't fly for me! I'm so sorry I hurt you little birdie!"

Granddaddy laughed at me tenderly and tried to explain.

"The bird is dead, Leah. It can't fly, ever again. I shot it with my cowboy gun so we can have food on the table. You didn't hurt him, though, so don't worry. Believe me. The bird did not feel any pain."

Although I stopped crying, I still didn't exactly understand death. However, I reasoned, whatever death was, it must not have been that bad since Granddaddy was laughing!

The days we spent on the farm in Beechgrove passed by very quickly. Lori and I didn't even seem to miss Mom as much as we once had. The thought of returning to our house in town didn't seem very appealing after having so much freedom and space on the farm. And neither one of us wanted to say "good-by" to our favorite "cowboy," Granddaddy.

He was my soul playmate, my very best friend! I needed him and I loved him with all my heart! He made me laugh, and he allowed me to think for myself, even if I messed up. He made me feel significant, not invisible.

That is, until that afternoon two years later when all of us were visiting the farm.

Awakening from my nap, I knew it would soon be time for another adventurous afternoon on the farm with my favorite Granddaddy.

I padded down the hall and knocked softly on his door, but there was no reply. I peered through the keyhole the best that I could, but all I could see was the figure of his body on top of his bed. Wow! How little he looked! When did he get so skinny?

I went down the hall and played with my dolls, waiting for him to wake up and play. I was lost in my own little world when I heard someone opening the front door to the porch.

Figuring that Granddaddy was finally ready to head for the barn to play, I quickly finished tucking away my toys and rushed outside to greet him with a big hug and a kiss. After all, he hadn't been feeling real well lately so it had been a long time since we had really been on an adventure together without MaMay around making a fuss.

Smiling and skipping around the house with my favorite dog, Corker, I saw Granddaddy climbing onto the back of his camper.

"Maybe we're going to go fishing or camping today!" I thought, full of excitement.

Slowing down to catch my breath, I caught a glimpse of something shiny in Granddaddy's hand. He was standing on the edge of the camper tailgate and looking down into the valley, across his beautiful farm towards the creek.

As he lifted his right hand towards his head, I recognized the shiny instrument in his hand as one his "cowboy guns."

"What was he doing playing without me?" I thought.

I started running up the little hill to the camper and was about to call out his name when I saw him place the gun to his head.

The piercing blast lanced my ears and echoed through the valley.

Granddaddy's body slumped to the ground below the camper, motionless.

I wasn't really frightened or anything. I was accustomed to hearing big, loud bangs coming from guns.

I slowly approached the place where Granddaddy's body rested, hesitating only when I saw the ground. It was covered in dark, red, icky looking stuff that resembled what Mom called "blood." I remembered this stuff from the time I cut my foot on a broken bottle. The red stuff looked the same, except this time there was a lot more of it.

Standing over Granddaddy's bloody and basically faceless body, I suddenly felt sad and alone. But unable to comprehend what had just happened, I began to laugh. I laughed and I laughed because that's what Granddaddy and I had always done together. We would always laugh — except this time.

A vision of the dead bird suddenly came to my mind because Granddaddy's body reminded me of that helpless bird which Granddaddy, himself, had explained to me was "dead." And now, just like that birdie that could never fly again, my grandfather would never play with me again.

"Who is going to laugh with me now?" I thought, my chuckles dying away.

As I saw my grandmother running out of the house towards us, I looked down at my favorite cowboy one more time.

All of a sudden furious at him for leaving me, I was aware of nothing else except that, once again, I would be alone.

"What had I done this time to drive the hero in my life away?" I wondered in little girl words, before I screamed at him as they dragged me away:

"I hate you! I hate you! I hate you for leaving me!"

Chapter Ten

The Trailer

I don't remember the first day that Jim became my stepfather.

Neither do I remember the first time he whipped me. But I do remember that I hated both occasions.

Few little girls like it when Mommy suddenly has a new husband, especially when the new one was so very different than the other one.

That was my earliest impression of my new "Daddy," however to me, he was never my "Daddy." Not even close. So I always called him "Jim."

Jim was, and still is, a brilliant man, a university professor, in fact. He could do almost anything he put his mind to, probably the reason why Mom fell in love with him.

Jim already had six children from his first marriage, and Mom had Lori and me, making eight. I suppose that still wasn't enough because together they had one more, so then there were nine!

My real daddy didn't like Jim, and I knew why. Soon after Mom married Jim, she allowed him to discipline us, thinking that young children needed a strong hand. Perhaps this is figuratively true, but not literally!

I do not remember what Lori and I did, but it must have been very "bad" because we received a BIG spanking from Jim. Lori and I were toddlers, about three and four years old. The story goes that our little buttocks were bruised from the whipping. And when visiting our daddy that weekend, he was furious at what he called "abuse." He immediately took us to a photographer in town who took pictures of the marks and bruises. Daddy said he planned to use the photos in court, testifying that his daughters were being unnecessarily and too severely punished. But the photographer backed out at the last minute, destroying the film. He said he didn't want to be involved.

So, what is "abuse?" Is punishing your children for something you feel they have done wrong abuse? Is instilling a strict work ethic and code of conduct abuse? Exactly what is abuse, and by what standards is it defined?

These are very difficult questions to answer, even to ask, especially when the person in question is your father figure. So, from the time I was about four until my mother finally divorced what I thought of as "the evil one" when I was in high school, these questions went unasked and unanswered by everyone, including myself and my mother.

It wasn't until I grew older, that it became apparent that Lori and I were being raised a bit different than our friends.

Who's to say what is right or wrong these days? I certainly can't say. But regardless, I simply began to feel cheated from my youth, and I blamed Jim.

He called us "boys."

We had to come straight home from school and go directly to work. At the crack of dawn on Saturdays and Sundays, we had to get up and go to work, and living on a farm, there was always something to be done or fixed.

Constantly, we had to haul hay, fix fences, feed the cows and other animals, dig potatoes, help bushhog, shuck corn, plow soybeans, vaccinate cattle, slaughter steers, kill pigs, package meat, chop wood, haul brush, build barns, chase mice, water the cows, put out the salt licks, drive the tractor, maintain the equipment, pull weeds, dig thistles, herd cattle, separate calves, go to market, plant the garden, dust the garden , pick the garden, can vegetables, string barbed wire fences, haul dirt, build gravel roads, and on and on. There was always something to be done!

Instilling a strong work ethic is very important, and operating a farm involves a lot of work for anyone. But, in my mind, Jim simply drove us too hard, punished us too severely, and showed us little love or compassion.

My worst public memory of Jim was one day when I was in the third grade.

I had invited twelve little girls home from school with me to celebrate my birthday. This was one of the most exciting events of my life because it was rare that girls from the city would come all the way out to my farm to play. And not only did I have a friend coming to play, I had twelve friends coming to play! Wow! I remember feeling like the most important person in the world! Even all the boys' April Fool's jokes didn't bother me that day!

I anxiously awaited for the three o'clock bell to ring. What a beautiful sound it was to my ears because I had been counting down the minutes for hours! All my friends gathered around me, smiling and giggling, holding their presents and birthday surprises in their hands. We all skipped happily outside and waited for my ride. I prayed Mom would be picking me up that day and not Jim; I didn't feel comfortable around him, and I thought he wouldn't let us laugh on the way home. As I saw our old station wagon round the curve, I breathed a thankful sigh as I recognized my mom in the car!

I was in heaven.

We sang songs, told jokes, and gossiped the entire long distance home. Most of the girls lived in the city and had never even visited a farm, thus everyone was extremely excited, especially me!

After topping the driveway and climbing out of the car, we all ran around the house like a bunch of chickens with their heads cut off. I gave my chattering entourage the grand tour of our little trailer, and a "bonus," a tour of MaMay's huge, log mansion!

Usually, I was embarrassed about living in the aluminum trailer because the boys at school always teased me cruelly about being a "Trailer Rat" and about my clothes stinking. Since we heated our home with a wood burning stove, our clothes smelled like smoke. But I didn't feel ashamed that day; I was just so proud to have friends in my own world!

My young friends enthusiastically asked a million questions and were most impressed that I knew so much about farms and animals. I answered question after question, and with each one I felt more and more confident and proud! I was on top of the world! Fun was being had by all, and I was the special person making it happen!

I decided we would run to the barn so I could show off my animals. Dodging cow piles and holding hands, we merrily sped down the hill. The sun was shining, the grass was spring fresh, and the smell of daffodils drifted along the worn, dirt path.

Inside the barn, I showed off some more by gathering a few eggs from the chickens. Now, not only was I the coolest girl in the third grade on this special day, but also I was the bravest. Chickens "cluck" very loud, so I had them all fooled that it was a dangerous and very rare feat to rob the nests of the eggs. I didn't tell them that the chickens were well accustomed to this little procedure!

Next, I showed them our one and only milk cow; we all giggled at the size of her teats. She was very full and needed to be milked, so once again I gave a quick demonstration of my amazing, "cow milking" ability. I didn't have the greatest success in hitting the bucket, but I received many brownie points for even daring to touch her pink teats!

Feeling that I could do nothing more to top the exciting extravaganza at the barn, we all voted to play on my jungle gym set up at the house.

Laughing till our bellies ached, we played on the swings and teeter totter. Some girls lined up on the slide and slid down together. Feet flying, hands clapping, and screams roaring, they all landed in a huge heap on top of each other on the ground! Others hung upside down from the monkey bars and pushed each other higher and higher in the swings. The excitement grew as we played, and so did the momentum. We were practically wild!

Having so much fun, and lost in a world of our own, we didn't notice that Jim had come home or that my little sister, Kara, had joined our circus of fun. She was still almost a baby, and had just begun to walk. I suppose all the giggling and warm cheers lured her from the safety of the house onto our crazy playground. Before I had even realized her presence, she toddled out in front of the big, metal swing. The pile of girls on the swing didn't even see her until Sid started barking. I looked up from the slide just in time to see her innocently stray too close to the swing.

I screamed as I leaped into the path of the swing, trying to protect her! She was so little, and the swing was so big and full of so many gals, I knew she would be hurt if the swing hit her. I managed to hurl my own body between Kara and the swing, knocking her safely out of the way.

Even though she was fine, the incident had really scared her! Immediately, Kara began to bawl loudly.

Interrupted from his work in the tool shed by Kara's frantic screaming, Jim suddenly came running out into the yard. He began verbally accosting me without even knowing what had happened. He deduced that I had been responsible for Kara's tears.

In front of all my friends on my very special day, he took off his belt and beckoned me to approach. I tried to stammer out the truth, but was too frightened. He wasn't listening anyway.

He grabbed me by my arm and whirled me around! Pulling down my pants and lecturing me about how "bad and evil" I was to allow Kara to get hurt, he whipped me six times.

I had never been so humiliated in my life.

My friends were still in shock; everything had occurred so fast that many were clueless as to what had just happened. I sobbed so heavily that I began to gasp for air. I didn't know what to do. Standing there crying, with my pants still down around my ankles, ashamed and embarrassed like never before, I started to rock. That's what I always did for comfort.

My friends also began to cry with me. I saw my dog run and hide under his favorite bush. For some reason, this seemed like the appropriate thing for me to do, too. I wanted to get away from everyone, but I had nowhere to go. So I quickly pulled up my pants and ran and crawled under the bush with my dog. And there we sat together until dinner. My friends tried to coax me into coming out sooner, but I was simply too mortified.

It was supposed to have been my day.

But it was now a disgrace.

And so was I, just as I was another day when I failed to protect my kitten.

Lori, Kara, and I had found the wild kittens in the barn. Lori chose a gray and white striped one. Kara chose the runt of the bunch, a yellow and white kitten. I chose the prettiest kitten of all, the pure white one with beautiful blue eyes.

She looked just like a powder puff, and felt just as soft as one. I named her Snowball, promising her I would be the best mother in the world!

A week later on a hot summer day, we were all so busy shucking corn, we didn't notice that our new kittens had come out from under the trailer to play. MaMay stood up from her seat in order to take a bucket of corn inside to boil, not seeing the little kittens as she stepped all over them. The kittens didn't know any better except to "meow," scratch and claw. So, that's what they did, attacking my granny's ankles and legs! It didn't hurt half as bad as it sounded, but they scratched her bad enough to make her bleed.

Without any warning, Jim picked up the closest kitten by the tail, lifted his powerful arm in the air and smashed its head on the concrete walk.

Shocked, in utter horror, we all stared in disbelief as the little body lay bloody and limp on the concrete.

Not knowing what to do, afraid to say anything, too scared to cry, I remember closing my eyes and continuing to shuck corn the best I could.

Chapter Eleven

Daddy's Girl

My real father was my salvation from evil.

He was also my knight in shining armor.

Daddy was the most loving, giving and sensitive man that I've ever known. A friend of his once wrote to me that my father was "much more than a man, he's a gentleman."

And that he was, having learned his impeccable manners and great respect for others from his mother, whom we called "Ishie."

These were the same values he taught Lori and me.

Although my Daddy was far from being wealthy, he was rich in spirit and heart. And he always found the money to pay Mom child support, and later, he helped us out whenever we needed a few extra dollars.

That was especially true after my mother finally divorced Jim. She always had to work really hard to make ends meet, and more often than not, there was no money for extra things for my sisters and me. I remember having to collect my thoughts and strength for weeks to ask Daddy if he would buy me a prom dress. He agreed to buy the material, if Mom would make it. So, I designed my own dress, dreaming of someday becoming a famous fashion designer, and Mom whipped it out. So while my dress was rather inexpensive, it was very original — and made from love .

Lori and I loved Daddy so much that we used to dream about living with him. In retrospect, it probably never was a real possibility, yet when times were miserable at home, thoughts of a life with Daddy gave me hope, an escape route of my dreams.

Although Lori and I were by no means "angels" around our father, we were better behaved in his presence. That's because we respected our Daddy's feelings and didn't want to disappoint him, unlike how we behaved around Jim, trying to act right because we were afraid of getting whipped.

Our Daddy just meant so very much to us, we valued every bit of time we shared with him, and we never, ever wanted to fall short of his expectations. And when we did stray, all Daddy needed to say was "Young ladies," and that was enough. From the time I was born, I can't remember a single time that he ever laid a hand on me.

So our weekends with Daddy were long anticipated. I fancied them as my "emancipation" from the "chains of slavery and darkness" living with Jim. From the moment Daddy picked us up on Friday afternoons until the time he brought us back home on Sundays, life was absolutely supreme. Daddy just had a magical way of making everything seem all right!

On Fridays when he picked us up, we would load our things in his big Oldsmobile and begin our drive to Shelbyville where we spent our weekends with Daddy and grandmother Ishie. A lot like her son, Ishie was the epitome of a strong, gentle, Southern woman, as well as a loving, doting grandmother.

I cannot describe to this day how good I felt to escape into their tender and affectionate refuge.

Ishie would always cook for us at every meal, and she would make us anything that we wanted. I remember always requesting hamburgers on Friday night. Lori always wanted applesauce and sausage on Saturday mornings. And Sundays after church, we'd have Daddy's favorite, fried chicken and mashed potatoes! Of course every night before going to bed, Daddy treated us to a big bowl of ice cream with cherries on top! I looked forward to this because not only did I get to fix everyone's dessert, I also had the honor of eating out of the "big spoon!" Daddy always teased me about talking so much, like my mother, so he said the huge, sterling silver spoon we used to scoop the ice cream was perfect for my big mouth!

The days shared with my Daddy are the most cherished memories that I have of my entire childhood.

You see, Daddy loved me unconditionally, and it was a love that blossomed in his every action. He was so proud to be our father and so happy just to be a significant part of our lives, he never took a single moment with us for granted. Later, without the loving balance that his affection taught me, I don't know how I would have survived some terrible times.

At night, Lori and I would bathe together in the huge, antique porcelain tub. After drying off with big, soft towels, Daddy would brush the tangles out of our hair and then softly dry it for us. He was always gentle, never pulling my hair like Mom did when she was putting my hair in pony tails. Then, Lori and I would play jacks on the warm, marble hearth as we watched shows like "The Love Boat" and "Fantasy Island." I loved those shows because they always had happy endings!

Daddy would tuck us into bed, and we would say our prayers together, out loud.

"Now I lay me down to sleep, I pray the Lord my soul to keep, if I should die before I wake, I pray the Lord my soul to take. God bless Daddy and Momma, Ishie and MaMay. God bless Jim, and all our brothers and sisters — Gerald, David, Cathy, Olan, Ellen, and Christie and Kara. And God bless all the animals in the world, bless all the good people and bless all the bad people, too, to help make them good. Please help us to be good little girls and keep our rooms clean. Bless God and Jesus too! Amen. P.S. Please let us go to Walt Disney World someday, but if we can't, Opryland will be okay. See you tomorrow. Good night."

Sometimes our prayers would go on and on, because Lori and I didn't like to leave out anyone. And we were afraid if we didn't ask God to bless them, then something bad might happen to them. Daddy patiently stayed by our bedsides and listened. When we were finally done, he kissed us on the forehead and told us he loved us.

I always slept so peacefully there. I was never really afraid, but even if I got a hint of being afraid, all I had to do was simply tiptoe into Daddy's room and crawl in bed beside him. I always thought I was doing this undetected, but I know now that he left his door open on purpose and that he moved his shoes out of the way because he knew I might be groggily stumbling through at any moment!

Sundays were always emotional and melancholy days for me.

Even now, I feel sad and lonely on this particular day because Sundays have always been "Good-bye days."

Before we began packing the car to head back to Beechgrove, a heavy-hearted feeling would dampen my spirit. We would all eat a last bowl of ice cream on the front porch, trying to make happy and light conversation. I always seemed to have to say farewell to the things I loved.

Our ride back to the farm was never as zestful as our trip away from there. Lori and I would sit as close to Daddy as we could, smothering him with hugs until we reached our long driveway. When I could see our trailer on the hill, I knew I was back in reality. A stinging in my chest would move up to become a lump in my throat. My hands would begin to get clammy, and my heart would beat a little faster. Trying to fight back the tears was no use. They came streaming down across my face, regardless.

Daddy would try to act cheerful and be strong for us. He never knew exactly what type of situation he was blindly placing us in. So, after hugging us repeatedly and incessantly telling us how much he adored us, he'd quickly unload the car and say those dreaded words that Lori and I neither one wanted to hear:

"Good-bye my little princesses. Daddy loves you!"

His voice would always crack.

Chasing his car down our long, curvy driveway, we ran! Running through the weeds and around trees, we ran as fast as our feet would take us, trying not to lose sight of his big, white car.

We waved and yelled:

"I love you, Daddy! I love you!"

Lori and I wouldn't stop the pursuit until his car was out of our sight and we heard his response — he honked his horn four times, our signal for "I love you, too."

Chapter Twelve

Searching for Me

When I was ready to begin high school, I transferred from Cascade, the school in the country near our farm, to Riverdale High School in Murfreesboro where Mom was a teacher.

I transferred for many reasons, but the major ones were that I didn't feel as if I "fit in" at Cascade and that my older sister Lori needed her space.

Although I had loved attending school at Cascade — the teachers were brilliant, as well as dedicated to education and genuinely concerned about the students' well being — the differences between Lori and me had begun to surface at school.

For the most part, while Cascade's family-type atmosphere enabled my academics to benefit greatly, it also placed Lori and me into a very small, competitive environment. Cascade was simply too small for both of us. We both needed room to grow and to spread our wings, independently of one another.

Even though Lori was only a year older than I, we had always been close until those precarious "teen years." But once we became classmates at the same junior high school, she acted as if she hated me! On the other hand, I had been very proud to finally become one of her "peers," as opposed to merely being her little sister!

But as most older sisters do, Lori made it obvious that I embarrassed her and that I wasn't welcome within her social circle. Strangely enough, I think she was most embarrassed by the style of clothes I chose to wear!

I never thought that I dressed any less than "fashionable," even though I'm sure it was a matter of taste! Yet, some people may have considered my attire unique because I often wore a lot of colorful outfits that I had bought in Europe as my clogging group danced in international Folklore Festivals.

And the styles in Europe were quite different from the styles of Bell Buckle, Tennessee!

So my flashy clothes were extremely novel.

And at conservative Cascade Junior High at that particular time, no one dared to be different in any way if they wanted to fit in with the right crowd and be accepted.

Since I actually was headstrong, determined to be different and unique, I was basically ostracized by all the other students, including my sister. So, after completing the eighth grade, I thought it was time for me to move on to a "larger pond!"

My transfer to the "big city" of Murfreesboro was smooth and fun. I had only been in school at Riverdale for a matter of weeks when the freshman class nominated me for Homecoming attendant. Wow! I couldn't believe it! I barely knew anyone, yet the class liked me enough to vote for me anyway! I just always smiled and tried to be friendly to everyone. It still amazes me how much a smile and an outwardly positive attitude can accomplish!

The first year at Riverdale was full of fun and excitement. I thought that life was as good as it could get.

I was popular, involved in many activities. I danced with the Rutherford County Square Dancers, and I worked for really good grades. And since Jim was no longer in my mother's life or mine, I felt happier and freer than I had ever remembered.

But I was already actively obsessed with food, I just wasn't worried about it so I don't remember it much.

I had few worries at all then beyond the normal high school concerns such as popularity and appearance.

Nonetheless, the self-esteem that had soared during my freshman year came to a screeching halt before the end of my sophomore year.

And although there may have been many contributing factors that led to this demise of my own self-image, the most significant single event occurred early in the fall of my second year at Riverdale.

My life would never be the same.

Chapter Thirteen

Halloween Hell

I remember my mother disturbing my studying, telling me to ride to Bell Buckle with Lori to pick up our younger sister Kara, who was out trick-or-treating with her friends.

I put my English composition away, irritated to be interrupted.

Academics were extremely important to me, especially English, and I had to devote most of my free time to my studies in order to earn the highest grades. Some people are naturally smart and don't have to study a lot in order to make good grades. I was not one of them. I had to work hard, and being a perfectionist, I had to work extremely hard if I realistically hoped to graduate as the Valedictorian of my class.

So I had passed up invitations to Halloween parties because my English paper was due the next week, and I wanted to finish it early so I wouldn't have to work on it during my weekend at Daddy's.

I had been so eager to get it done, I hadn't even changed out of my school clothes, black slacks and a silk, button-down blouse.

A few minutes later, Lori and I were riding toward Bell Buckle, passing small groups of giggling children running door to door in their costumes.

As a young child, I had loved Halloween — especially the candy! But I had also heard all the stories of ghosts, witches and magic. They scared me.

Already intensely afraid of the dark, I always begged to sleep with Lori on every Halloween night, even after getting a bit older. And for some reason, I had nightmares that something evil was going to happen to me on Halloween night, October 31, 1983.

But nothing in my wildest imagination could have compared to the real events of that dreadful night.

Lori and I parked the car along a well-lighted street in Bell Buckle, waiting for Kara to finish her trick-or-treating.

Before long, Lori caught a glimpse of some of her friends, and we both scrambled out of the car to greet them. We all stood around talking for a while, but since Lori and her friends went to a different school than I, I didn't easily fall into the conversation.

After a while, I decided to go back and sit on the car, which was about 30 feet away.

Once there, to stay warm and make time pass faster, I began practicing a few dance steps and cheers that I had recently learned at cheerleading practice.

I was so involved in my own thoughts that I didn't notice the gang of boys from the "Hill" approaching. When I heard Lori and her friends laughing and screaming good-naturedly, I looked up to see eight or ten guys, ranging in age from about 15 to 28, chasing an old friend of mine named David, pelting him with water balloons. I watched the "chase" with instinctive curiosity.

The gang continued to taunt and chase David, attracting a small audience of observers, until they caught and tackled him on the ground of leaves. Then mercilessly, they smeared him with everything gross they had with them — eggs, dishwashing soap, syrup, whip cream, ketchup, mustard, you name it. It was insanely gross and nasty, and all the leaves that began sticking all over him made it worse!

The astonished spectators watched from a distance, but their laughter abruptly stopped as the gang rushed into the small crowd, throwing eggs and spraying whip cream on them, too.

I wanted to go home, but my little sister was still nowhere in sight.

Suddenly, my attention returned to the gang when I heard a raspy voice scream:

"Get that one! Get her! She thinks she's too good for us, all dressed up like that! Get her!!!"

At first, it didn't quite register that the gang had now directed their eyes toward me. I was just dancing around under the street light, minding my own business, waiting for my sister. What had I done to provoke their attention and to become a new target?

As the gang headed my way, I recognized a few faces from when I had attended school at Cascade, but they looked fierce and aggressive. Realizing they meant business, and not wanting all that icky stuff sprayed all over my good clothes, my instinct was to run.

So, without having time to think, I began running, trying to escape from their fury of sick Halloween pranks.

I ran as fast as I could go, but I could hear their screams and laughter closing in on me quickly. At the end of the street, they began to circle around me! I spotted a trail into the woods — my only option for escape!

Somehow, I managed to maneuver through the gang and dart into the woods, unsoiled! Never thinking that they would continue this foolish sport and actually follow me into the woods, I slowed down to catch my breath. The woods were really dark and rather thick. I began to doubt if I could find my way back out of the labyrinth of trees and foliage. But that fear was rapidly replaced by a figure jumping out from behind a huge tree!

As he laughed, all I could see were the whites of his bulging eyes and his shining teeth!

Hoping I could reason with this guy to halt the ridiculous chase, I made a vain attempt to strike up conversation. But it was useless. My voice was soon drowned out by the loud cajoling of the rest of the wildly crazed gang. Hearing their incessant and vulgar taunts, my rising hysteria sent me running once again! The chase pursued as they followed me deeper and deeper into the woods.

I ran in a panic until I stumbled on the dark, uneven dirt. Picking myself up instantly, I started running again.

Before long, my lungs felt like they were about to explode. Having lost one of my shoes when I had fallen down, I was stumbling, disoriented in the dark woods, not knowing which way to go! Soon, I was running in circles.

Every time I'd wheel one way, a face would jump out from behind a tree! I'd whirl the other way, and another smiling, crazy face would appear before my eyes! I grew dizzier and dizzier as I began to feel an eerie, frightening sense of complete helplessness.

But still not wanting to believe the true intentions of my frenzied stalkers, even though their brutal cajoling had caused me to become fearful of the worst, I instinctively screamed out for Lori. She couldn't have been more than 100 yards away, and she had to hear me — but she thought my cries for help were nothing more than trying to escape being sprayed by the gang's mess of eggs and whip cream.

Pounding hard against the firm ground, I felt my body fall!

I tasted the bitter flavor of blood as my teeth chomped down on my tongue. My legs and arms were stinging from sticks and twigs as my body was being wrestled about. I kicked my legs trying to ward off the hands I felt all over my body as my attackers smeared toothpaste and eggs all over me. Twisting and turning and jerking my head trying to free my hair and arms from their clutches, I pleaded for them to stop hurting me!

I could hear myself screaming.

Then, the real horror began.

I felt my shirt torn from my body and sharp sensations stung my chest as I helplessly struggled more and more! My arms were useless, pinned down cruelly above my head. I kept screaming for Lori until I started choking on dirt and leaves. Then I closed my eyes tightly, praying that what I had begun to fear couldn't possibly be happening to me! But deep down, I knew this was turning into something much more than a Halloween joke.

The fiendish laughter grew unbearably loud. I heard heavy breathing all around me, as if I were in a vacuum. Time seemed to stand still as I felt hands pawing me as if I were a piece of dirt.

"Stop! Please!" I managed to plead frantically.

Fingers curled tightly around my throat. Coughing and choking on blood, I thought I was going to die.

Suddenly, I froze.

I heard the sound of my zipper coming unzipped. Until that moment, I had never really listened to that particular sound nor noticed how loud it was. Now, I heard the small piece of metal pass over every single tooth of the zipper. As if it were thunder, I shuttered from the force of the earsplitting sound.

"Please, God," I prayed. "Please make me invisible! Save me from this!"

A sudden coldness and wetness on my back and legs quickly brought me back to the reality of the moment. I knew then that my bra had come unhooked, and my pants were down.

My arms were still useless, pinned over my head. My wrists were tingling from loss of circulation. And my pants had found their resting place around my ankles.

Opening my eyes, my vision was blocked by the many faces of my attackers surrounding me. Their faces seemed grotesque and distorted by my own dazed state. Even though I couldn't make any clear distinctions at that point, I could feel their every presence — they were everywhere! Groaning, laughing, cheering, and ribbing each other on, they became more violent. I could see their wicked smiles, their teeth and even their gums. I could feel their hands harshly touching me, grabbing me and rubbing me! The smell of alcohol was present as they breathed heavily in my face and in my ears and as they bit and kissed my face and neck!

Each assailant seemed to want to go a bit farther.

It was then that I felt a stinging, cold sensation penetrate my body! I couldn't believe this was happening!

I felt rough fingers inside me, groping and scratching. It hurt terribly, but the pain of realizing what could further happen to me was insurmountable! Wet tongues were licking me all over, especially my stomach! My mouth was covered with repugnant kisses.

"How could so many hands be assaulting me at once?"

It seemed like every inch of my body was being ravaged and mutilated at once! Then, the throbbing torture piercing me so severely overwhelmed my brain. I could hardly feel anything anymore, even the repeated burning sensations of further violations.

I just prayed, over and over again, for God to help me.

Finally, he must have heard my prayers. I opened my eyes once again, and I was able to make direct eye contact with a face I recognized.

"Please, Tyrone, please! We used to be friends, remember? Please make them stop! Please! I used to help you with your homework in study hall, remember? I was your friend! And I still am! Please, make them stop, and I promise that I won't tell anyone! Please!"

Gasping for any air at all, I hyperventilated. I felt my coherence fade and soon everything around me went blank. I drifted into a calmer, more peaceful world. I felt as if I were floating.

I don't know where I drifted nor for how long, but when I awoke I was all alone.

I laid there, scared, and confused in a heap of dead leaves.

I could see the stars. They looked so bright, so beautiful, but so far out of reach. How I wished I were a shining star!

Instead, I felt insignificant, dirty, soiled and ashamed!

There was nothing to do but pull my dirty pants up over my bruised and bleeding body. I straightened my silk blouse, now soiled and ripped, as best that I could while looking for my shoes. As I searched the ground in the dark, I saw the empty remnants of the barbaric night — broken egg shells, toothpaste tubes, syrup bottles, whip cream cans and spoons.

I slumped to the ground, holding my knees to my chest as I began to rock back and forth.

"Leah!" I heard Lori call. "Where are you? I've been waiting for you forever! Come on!"

I couldn't make a sound.

Minutes later, Lori was standing above me.

"Oh my God, Leah! Oh my God! What happened?"

"They grabbed me and ripped my shirt and scared me. That's all."

No other words were spoken.

She picked me up to my feet, held my hand and guided me back through the dark woods. We drove home in silence, except for the sounds of my heaves as I vomited on myself.

Once home, I tried to make it to my room without Mom seeing me, but she came bouncing out of the house to greet us with a big smile.

The moment she saw me, her smile vanished.

My long, blonde hair was matted to my forehead and face. My shirt was ripped and stained. My feet were bare because I was holding the single shoe I could find.

I answered Mom's questions the same way I did Lori's. She told Lori to start a hot shower for me, as she put her arms around me, hugging me tightly. She cradled me there for a long time, whispering that it was not my fault.

She said all the right things, but when I stumbled into the bathroom and looked in the mirror, I hated myself.

"You are evil, Leah!" I said. "You are evil and wicked! Why did you let that happen?"

I took a scalding hot shower before I returned to the mirror, naked and dripping wet.

"I will never think about this again, never!" And I vowed to never tell anyone what had really happened.

Performing tactical maneuvers as part of her ROTC training, Hulan carries her M-16 rifle through the woods.

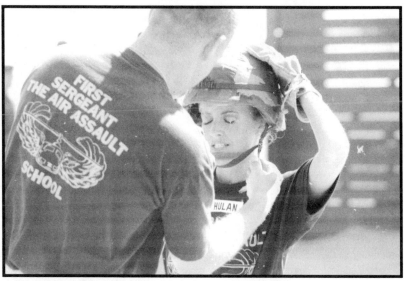

Hulan receives assistance with her helmet from the First Sergeant of the Screaming Eagles Air Assault School.

Hulan (front, center) with fellow Screaming Eagles at Air Assault School in Fort Campbell, Kentucky.

A beauty queen in combat boots, Hulan poses with members of the Colombia police force.

Hulan proudly salutes a receptive audience after being crowned Miss Knoxville 1992 (prelim. to Miss America).

Hulan, a newly-crowned Miss Tennessee USA™, salutes in appreciation to her grandmother who she had just learned had been injured in a car accident.

Prior to Miss Tennessee interview, Hulan strikes a military-inspired pose.

During her reign as Miss Tennessee USA™, Hulan poses with then Congressman Don Sundquist and wife Martha before a fundraiser. Sundquist later became Governor of Tennessee.

During the swimsuit competition, Hulan stands beside Lu Parker, Miss USA 1994.

Hulan and other pageant contestants with Kathie Lee Gifford at the Miss America Pageant™ in Atlantic City.

Hulan and her mom "tackle" Joe Theismann.

Hulan with Regis Philbin at the Miss America Pageant™ rehearsals.

Miss Tennessee Teen USA™ Allison Alderson, 1994, Michael Bolton, and Kim and Lee Greenwood following a concert.

Hulan and former Miss Tennessees with Governor Ned McWherter at the Governor's Mansion

Pageants

Hulan performs her clogging routine during the Miss Tennessee pageant in Jackson.

Hulan models in a fashion show before the Miss America pageant.

Hulan after the 1990 Miss MTSU Pageant, her first pageant.

Hulan appears calm and relaxed backstage before the Miss Tennessee Pageant™

(Below) Hulan and Kimberly Greenwood (wife of singer Lee Greenwood, and Jaime Nicole Dudney, Miss Tennessee Teen USA™ 1993, and the daughter of Barbara Mandrell.

At 102 lbs., Hulan appears confident and self-assured during the swimsuit competition at the Miss USA Pageant™.

Youth

Hulan in a sixth-grade photograph.

Hulan poses before a dance recital (5th grade).

Hulan as a nursery school youngster.

Hulan with date Michael Morgan before a high school dance. (Look at that hair!)

While at Cascade High School, Hulan presents a positive, anti-drug message to the student body.

Hulan delivers her message to the Chamber of Commerce in her hometown of Murfreesboro, Tennessee.

Hulan speaks to a receptive audience at the Governor's Mansion in Nashville.

Hulan delivers a poignant message to soldiers of the 30th Separate Armor Brigade in West Tennessee.

Hulan with her Aunt Polly at her Homecoming in Murfreesboro.

Hulan poses with an admiring fan.

During her stay in Colombia, Hulan visits a local orphanage.

Hulan smiles for a publicity photo while serving herself brunch at The Miss America Pageant™.

Hulan with her ex-fiance, CPT Tom Bertrand.

While waiting for her sister, Hulan gave in to her temptation to binge. She devoured almost the entire pizza before her sister returned and caught her "sneaking" food.

Miscellaneous

Proudly displaying their Army fatigues are Hulan and ex-fiance, then 2 Lt. Tom Bertrand, at the Military Intelligence Officer Basic Course.

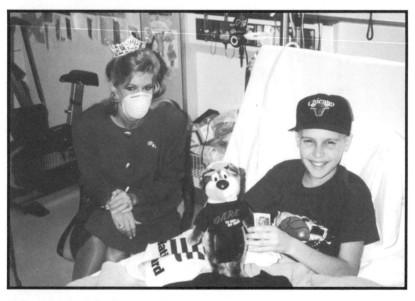

Hulan visits young fan Daniel Brantley in the hospital while he was undergoing treatment for leukemia at Vanderbilt Hospital.

Hulan with a new friend and roommate, Miss North Dakota, at the Miss USA™ Pageant.

Hulan had her own trading card at the Miss America Pageant.

Hulan poses with mom and sister Kara Kemp after winning Miss Tennessee USA™ 1994.

Miscellaneous

A family portrait: grandmother MaMay, Hulan, younger sister Kara, older sister Lori, and mom Marcia.

Teenagers Hulan and sister Lori with their dad.

A tender moment between sisters.

Chapter Fourteen

Who Am I?

When I made that pact with myself that horrible Halloween night, I neglected to realize one thing.

Even if I could ignore — and perhaps even forget many of the vulgar details of the assault — that wasn't enough.

Unless I dealt with it head-on, unless I could realize the assault was not my fault, I would never be free of the inferior, disgraceful feelings of self-reproach and self-disgust.

But it wasn't until years later, when I was forced to seek counseling, that I begin to escape the memories of that night.

Thus, for years and years, I wasn't sure about a lot of things, mainly myself. And all the memories I tried to block out simply kept on flying around like evil ghosts inside my head, affecting my judgment, my trust, my happiness and, consequently, my self-esteem.

The seeds of evilness and disgrace had been planted. Until I was ready to confront them and face the circumstances of my past, I would continue to see myself as they made me feel on the inside — loathsome, vile, unworthy, shameful, undeserving, a failure!

And my self-imposed punishment was food, either mountains of it at one sitting or none at all, for days or weeks.

It was after that Halloween night that I began distancing myself from my classmates. On the outside, it wasn't a major change in life since I had never established very close bonds with any of my schoolmates. Also, because we lived so far out in the country and often had to go straight home after school, my isolation wasn't obvious. But on the inside, my depressed attitude was very apparent.

I felt inferior to my schoolmates, especially the girls who were on the cheerleading squad with me. For some reason, I just never felt like I fit in. I felt totally alone in my tarnished existence.

Anyway, I had something else to occupy my mind , food.

So, even if I did well, I never could accept any triumphs. Even when I was voted "Most Outstanding Girl" every year in high school, I still felt "different" and undeserving.

Simply, I hated myself.

But I hid it well.

I was very ambitious and definitely a perfectionist, and I continued to push myself to reach greater and greater heights. Socially, I was always gregarious and everyone's pal, yet away from crowds, I kept to myself and coveted my isolation.

So, hating myself, despising my appearance because I saw myself as fat, my bouts with anorexia and bulimia became more and more frequent. Even though I had indulged in both diseases for years, this particular point in my life was when the true fracas with Bulimarexia began.

With every passing day that I sheltered my ugly secrets, I became more at the mercy of this disease. If I attempted to feel important and meaningful through my growing ambitions, it seemed like new, opposing forces emerged to knock me back further than I had been before. I felt incapable of controlling my own growth, my own existence.

So as a teenager, I attributed my Bulimic vomiting in high school primarily to my self-perception of being fat and ugly. Of course, I realize now that there was much more to it than that. I only wish that it could have been that simple.

Nonetheless, it was during my last high school years that my Bulimic tendencies began to take on a life of their own. I simply could not ignore my natural hunger any longer, and my inability to turn down food provoked me to eat. So, I would eat enough to satiate my hunger, and then go to the bathroom and throw up. I never considered the destruction that I was doing to my body. This conduct had become a normal part of my life.

Also, since I've always been able to rid my stomach of food merely by thinking how fat I was and about how "bad" I was for eating, I've never had to induce vomiting by artificial means. Sticking my finger down my throat until gagging or using diuretics and laxatives have never been necessary for me. I could purge on command. This helped me avoid analyzing my behavior. But even that led to other problems.

Because my body often automatically vomited food when it reached the confines of my stomach, sometimes I could not control when or where I was going to throw up.

I remember having a date to our basketball homecoming game with a really good friend named Rick. He and I had actually grown up together, but this was our first attempt at a romantic date, and I really wanted to impress him. We doubled-dated with two really good friends of mine, Miriam and her date Clay, and we all had a fantastic time.

We had eaten dinner at an exquisite restaurant and then had proceeded to the dance. After dancing the night away with Rick, I developed a huge crush on him! Anyway, Clay and Rick drove Miriam and me to my grandmother's house. They escorted us up to the door where Clay kissed Miriam and Rick kissed me good night.

I was absolutely in Heaven! Wow! Rick kissed me! Rick actually kissed me and it was awesome! Miriam and I both jumped around, giggling with excitement!

Suddenly, only seconds after Rick had kissed me, I was doubled over with my head hidden in the bushes, coughing and heaving up my dinner. I hadn't even thought about trying to purge my food yet. I had no idea I was going to get sick. Miriam, who was shocked and rather grossed out, said:

"Leah Hulan! You almost puked in his mouth! He wasn't even out of the driveway before you were vomiting your brains out! You better get control of your little problem, or at least don't humiliate me by asking me to double with you again!"

Miriam was a cheerleader with me and had been aware that I had been purging after eating meals. I still thought nothing of what she said except that I merely would not ask Miriam to spend the night with me again.

Pushing friends away became a way of life.

Chapter Fifteen

The Mask

I began wearing way too much makeup.

As a dancer spending a significant amount of time "on stage," I think I had grown accustomed to wearing my "stage face" even when I wasn't performing.

Boundless with energy and momentum as I danced, I loved being an entertainer and being the center of attention. I soon became addicted to the limelight because all the attention and constant praise made me feel appreciated, at last. I felt as if I had finally found something that I could do extremely well!

Dancing created a new identity for me that I loved because everyone else seemed to love the gal they watched perform on stage. As our dancing group toured around the states and then in Europe, I thought my chest would burst with pride during our standing ovations in Spain and France! Watching people clap their hands, tap their feet and whistle enthusiastically to the beat of the music as I performed my solo dance became my fuel for life!

On stage, I felt confident, professional, and beautiful — totally unlike the person that I felt off the stage.

Soon, I began to associate success with my stage identity and began wearing more and more make-up when I was nowhere near a stage. Before I realized it, I was unable to leave the house until I had applied my "ton of paint." It was the only way that I felt pretty and accepted by others.

Of course I heard people whispering behind my back about my excessive use of make-up, but I couldn't stop wearing it. I had begun to hide behind the mask. There, no one could see the real Leah. No one could see the secrets and shame. Even the mirror reflected a different image than the one I knew existed under the mask. With the make-up, I was safe and could pretend to be free.

But one day, after my mother had grown embarrassed for me because I continued to wear such an extreme amount of make-up, she forbade me to wear any at all. I would have disobeyed her and worn it anyway if I could have. But she was my French teacher in high school and obviously would have caught me when I came to class.

I remember driving to school with her that day, feeling completely horrified at the thought of people seeing me without my make-up. It wasn't merely a feeling of looking unattractive, I felt broken, desperate, shameful and extremely vulnerable. I cried all the way to school. Then, scared and intimidated by the thought of walking down the halls among all my peers looking so gross, I hid in the bathroom and skipped two classes. But I had Mom's French class for third period, and I knew I couldn't skip her class. Hanging my head as low as it would go and keeping my eyes to the floor, I slid down the hallway to class as discreetly as possible. In class, the kids all knew something was terribly wrong because there was a lot of tension in the air between my mother and me. After all, she was the one who had caused me to suffer this way by forbidding me to apply even a bit of powder, and I was miserable! My eyes were already red and swollen from crying, and classmates began to inquire what was wrong. I burst into hysterical tears, and once again fled to the solace of the bathroom.

Until that very moment, Mom had been unaware of the depth of my low self-esteem and how dependent I had become on make-up to shape my identity. She had merely thought that I was going through a teenage phase that I would soon get over it. But seeing how crushed and belittled I felt without my "mask" to hide behind, she sent the guidance counselor to talk to me.

After talking only a short while with the counselor, she suggested that I be allowed to wear the "war paint" if I needed it that badly — even if I did look terrible with so much of it on.

It was a victory, but an empty one.

I had ceased to exist without the comfort and attention that I thought the make-up brought me.

As soon as the counselor left, I rushed over to the mirror and quickly applied my "face."

Chapter Sixteen

Skipping Senior Year

During my junior year in high school, I scored high enough on my ACT to attend college classes during my senior year.

I decided that this would be a practical choice for me. I had planned to major in foreign languages in college, and I had already taken all the advanced French classes that were offered in high school. Starting college early would enable me to continue my French studies without a breech in my education, and it would also allow me to commence accruing college credit. Since the local college, Middle Tennessee State University, had such a commendable foreign language department, I began college classes in the Fall of 1985.

Academically speaking, I benefited a great deal from entering college early. But, in retrospect, the negative consequences of this decision far out-weighed the positive results.

I was only 17 years old and lacked the confidence and responsibility necessary to do well in college.

I remember being so frightened as I parked my car on campus that I would start sweating. Just walking to class was a chore, too. All the other students seemed so powerful and perfect. I felt ugly in their presence and did not feel like I belonged. I still had braces on my teeth, and I was so self-conscious about them that I didn't dare smile. I would just bolt to class everyday with my head down and my eyes fixed steadily on my feet.

Participating in classes was an even greater obstacle for me than getting up enough nerve to walk to class. I had never before had problems speaking up in class, but suddenly I was petrified to ask or answer any questions. The one time I did muster up the courage to ask a question, the professor laughed at the question, humiliating me. My confidence plummeted even more. I became so nervous just thinking about having to participate again in class that I would literally get sick. So, I began skipping classes more and more, until mercifully, the semester was over.

Having been so accustomed to getting straight A's in high school, I was shocked when I received two A's, a B and, heaven forbid, a D. But I didn't care — I was just thankful the ordeal was over! I would have the entire summer to rebuild my confidence before heading off to my real college of choice, Converse College in Spartanburg, South Carolina.

Looking back, I should never have bypassed by my senior year. I missed that level of confidence students usually develop during their senior year when they are finally the "big shots." But I never felt like the "big fish" in a small pond. Instead, I was a guppy in the oceán.

Because of my good grades in high school, I was lucky enough to earn a scholarship to Converse, an outstanding, all-female school which is noted for its foreign language curriculum that offers great opportunities to study abroad. The thought of attending an all-girls' school appealed to me because I had never really had the opportunity to develop strong relationships with girls my own age. Even though I had friends who were girls, my living far away on the farm combined with my tomboy interests and inferiority complex kept me from learning how to be comfortable around most females. Also, though unknown to me then, my mother thought that attending an all-girls' college might boost my self-esteem — at least enough to quit hiding behind my mask of makeup.

I absolutely loved Converse. I was challenged academically and my grades were great.

But even though I was ready to open myself up to establishing bonds with other girls, I wasn't ready to sacrifice my privacy. For that reason, I paid extra fees enabling me to have a single room.

Although Converse helped me increase my confidence — I actually stopped wearing makeup at all — there were certain negative aspects of the school that stimulated my bulimia more than ever.

Like most colleges, the upper-class students at Converse warned us freshmen of the infamous "Freshman Fifteen," the term referring to the amount of weight a freshman girl usually gained during her first semester in college. At the time, I didn't see how I could ever gain that much weight so rapidly as long as I maintained some type of normal fitness routine. But like many other girls, I easily fell victim to the pattern of college eating.

Being away from home and free to party and drink a lot of beer were the reasons many of my classmates gained weight. But, of course, my strongest temptation wasn't alcohol. It was food.

At Converse, there were no choices of meal plans. All food was served in the dining hall. At meal time, the doors opened and endless tables were heaped with almost every food imaginable! The hot line was always open, consisting of steaming vegetables and a variety of casseroles and meats. And there was the most incredibly delectable salad bar that I'd ever seen in my life, including baked potato and Mexican bars, complete with all the toppings. Beyond that, there were other tables covered with every type of fruit possible, plus a wall lined with large barrels of a dozen different kinds of cereal, available at every meal.

To top things off, there were two soft-serve ice cream machines and two banquet tables piled high with cookies, cakes, cobblers and brownies galore, made fresh from the kitchen! I simply could not resist all this amazing food on display before my hungry eyes.

I had to sample everything, then go back for seconds! Also, since the dining facility was only open at mealtimes, we learned early to sneak a few goodies into our pockets for later. It was against the rules, but who could help from wrapping a few dozen cookies up in a napkin for a midnight snack? Certainly not me!

It's easy to see how I suddenly gained weight. In fact, I gained so much so fast, I hadn't noticed that I had ballooned until all my clothes were entirely too small. But that problem was easily solved, or at least hidden. At an all-girls' school, there's no reason whatsoever to roll out of bed a second before five minutes to class time. There were no boys around, so why bother getting up early to take a shower, put on makeup and dress nicely for class? So the unofficial uniform at Converse was the oldest, yuckiest, most worn-out pair of sweat pants you owned.

As I gained weight by splurging at the dessert table at every single meal, I concealed the pounds from myself and the world in my oversized sweat suits. It worked, perhaps too well. Even I was almost unaware of my excessive weight gain until I went home at Christmas. But boy, then I found out in a hurry!

I knew I had become a fat pig when both my typical, Southern grandmothers complimented me on how "healthy" I looked.

That was, indeed, the kiss of death! My bulimia, which had been dormant for several months, reared up again, stronger than ever.

The only thing that halfway saved me occurred the next semester when I began taking Reserve Officers Training Corps or ROTC classes at Wofford College, a neighboring school with primarily all male students. And the Wofford ROTC program was swelling over with handsome college cadets, something that practically beckoned me to join! It was, after all, the easiest way to meet guys! But beyond that, I already had some of the skills they teach in the first two years by having been a tomboy, growing up on a farm.

In the ROTC program, not only did we participate in competitive physical training, but we also did things like white water rafting, rifle shooting and rappelling.

When we practiced "grass drills" and maneuvers during training exercises in the mountains, I was in heaven!

And I found something in the program that I had never found anywhere else — a sense of belonging.

Just hanging around military people and talking "Army" was very interesting and patriotically inspiring to me. I thought I had found my niche in society.

Yet, after three semesters at Converse, I packed my bags for Tennessee where I re-enrolled at MTSU.

I had, or at least I thought I had, fallen in love.

Chapter Seventeen

Uncle Sam and Me

His name was Bobby. He was several years older than I.

And our relationship was a disaster.

Almost as soon as I moved back home, Bobby become insanely obsessive and jealous. He wanted to manipulate my every move. He was cruel about anything I did other than catering to him, and before I knew it, he had begun to physically abuse me.

With each smack and slap, I felt more and more unworthy; I felt like I was nothing. I thought failure might as well have been my middle name. I had ruined everything. I had sacrificed my education at Converse, consequently giving away my goal of studying abroad in France.

And even though I did everything in my power to show Bobby how much I loved him, it was never enough, so I felt as if I had failed him, too. When he broke up with me, his total rejection was devastating.

I felt like the worst person in the world.

Rejoining the ROTC program was the only thing that saved me from self-destruction.

All along, I had planned to continue in the ROTC program but merely as an non-obligated participant. That meant I was only taking classes for college credit and had not signed a contract to serve in the Army after graduation. But as I became more involved in the ROTC program, I started to feel little seeds of confidence and self-esteem.

More than anything, being a ROTC cadet forced me to follow a very strict, regimented code of physical fitness. And soon, I was even feeling a little bit of pride in myself.

When I began the program at M.T.S.U., I could barely run two miles at a stretch and could only do about ten push-ups correctly. Three months later, I had lost about 10 pounds, and my stamina had improved drastically. And the new ability to run long distances and to do more than sixty push-ups in only 2 minutes was a huge boost to my self-esteem, and also made me very competitive with my peers.

So I buried myself in ROTC. And the more I learned about the military, the more I liked it. I applied for a two-year ROTC scholarship that would pay for my tuition and books. Accepting the scholarship meant I would have to sign a contract to agree to serve in the U.S. Army after graduation.

It was the biggest decision that I had ever made in my life.

After carefully weighing my options, I decided to take the plunge! The factor that tugged at me the strongest was that I had earned this opportunity all by myself, and it was based on my potential and my merit alone! For a girl harboring a sinking ship of self-esteem, winning this scholarship was like a turning point in my battle to be worthy.

That summer, after Bobby left me, I began exercising, almost non-stop.

I ran in the mornings. I ran at lunch. I ran in the evenings. I rode my bike everywhere and entered several biathalons. I totally absorbed myself in physical fitness, with a hidden thought in the back of my mind: "If only Bobby could see me now!"

I continued in this silly routine until my grandmother, MaMay, thought it was time to stop the foolishness. She remembered that earlier in the school year, I had mentioned an opportunity to study for several months in Canada at the Universite de Laval in Quebec. But Bobby had refused to allow me to seriously consider the summer course, so I basically forgot about it until MaMay extended a wonderful offer.

Just to get my mind off Bobby, she would finance my tuition, room and board and my travel expenses if I would go. How could I refuse that kind of offer?

The semester I spent in Quebec was probably the most beneficial semester of my entire college years. Not only did I do well in my French studies because of this immersion experience, I also found a new sense of "being" during those beautiful days in Canada. Free from commitments, free from any real type of responsibility, and free from pressure, I was also free to be me! I actually saw myself change from the helpless puppy, running scared with her tail tucked between her legs, into a brave, newborn colt, trying to test her shaky, new legs in an unfamiliar world.

And the person who helped me most was a handsome Canadian named Dean, who was in a more advanced class than mine.

Our relationship was innocent and without pressure. Dean made me laugh. And he was one of the first men whom I'd ever known who liked me for my friendship and wanted nothing in return for his.

As the summer progressed, I became ever more thankful for my grandmother's assistance and insistence that I go to Canada. Although I often thought about Bobby, I was far enough away to find a balance to keep me out of depression. Much of this new-found balance came from Dean.

I remember one night we started talking about what we wanted to do with the rest of our lives. Dean's dreams included returning to his family's homeland of Israel and working in his uncle's business. I admired his loyalty to family and culture very much. My dreams were just as loyal to family and culture, but they didn't seem nearly as exciting as going to Israel. I told him I simply wanted to return home, manage the farm, and take care of my family.

Dean, who was very perceptive, said:

"Who are you trying to fool, Leah? You are someone who will not be happy unless you are running around with your hair on fire trying to change the world. And you are too co-dependent on people to find happiness in isolation. You need to help people because you need to be needed. That's how you became involved in that abusive relationship. You feel like you can love someone enough to help them. But you've got to learn to look after yourself first. Then, you can do whatever you want to do and be anything you want to be."

I had heard the words before, but I had never really listened.

For a month or so, it actually seemed like I was making some sense out of my life.

By the end of summer, I was more excited than ever about returning home.

I was anxious to conquer the world!

Chapter Eighteen

Saying Goodbye

I was on cloud nine when I stepped off the plane in Nashville.

Mom, Daddy, MaMay, Lori and Kara were there to pick me up, and they all seemed quite happy that I had conquered my depression as they listened to me ramble on and on about my future plans.

Then, I became aware of a profound silence in the car. Usually, my mom and sisters and I are so talkative, no one else can squeeze in a single word.

But no one was talking but me.

At first, I thought perhaps Mom and Daddy were simply uncomfortable being in the same car together, even though they had an amiable relationship.

But then I looked at Lori's eyes, and I could see they were red and swollen. I knew if Lori wasn't laughing, that was a clear indication that something was definitely wrong.

When we arrived at my grandmother's house, everyone methodically helped me unload all my suitcases from the car before scurrying straight inside the house. Basically, I was left standing alone outside wondering what the hell was going on!

When I followed my family into the house, they all just stood around awkwardly looking at each other.

Finally, Daddy broke the silence by asking me to accompany him into the living room. The dread in our steps made the hallway seem miles long.

"Sit down, Leah," Daddy said gently.

I remember the hall light shining on his face as he calmly began his obviously rehearsed speech.

While I was in Canada, Daddy had visited the doctor for his yearly check-up. During the exam, a dark spot about the size of a nickel was discovered on one of his lungs. Further tests indicated that the small mass was cancerous. Surgery was necessary immediately.

As he spoke these words, I felt the life being drained from my veins.

Cancer. My father, my hero, had cancer!

As I tried to regain my composure, Daddy whispered in my ear how much he loved me and how much he needed his little princess to be strong for him.

He hugged me and squeezed me tightly one more time before saying that he was tired and needed to get some rest. I followed him out the door. As his car left the driveway, I ran after him, yelling "I love you!"

I heard him honk the horn four times, our old familiar sign.

I was devastated.

I was alone again.

Daddy went into surgery the following week at Vanderbilt Hospital in Nashville. The surgery was said to be a great success, with the doctors saying they felt sure they had removed all of the malignant mass before it had spread. But tests proved differently. The cancer had already spread to other parts of the body. Chemotherapy and radiation were the only hopes.

Daddy moved in with my grandmother MaMay and me. Since she was his ex-mother-in-law, some of her friends ribbed her lightheartedly about Daddy living with us; but he was too weak to live alone.

I spent all my free time with Daddy. I would do my homework in his room and sometimes take my ROTC combat boots in to get a few pointers on the correct way to "spit shine" them.

"Never in a million years did I think I'd see the day when my baby girl would be wearing combat boots!" he teased.

We spent some of the most tender times of our lives together over the next few months. But alone, I knew Daddy was worried about dying, and I began exercising to the extreme.

Every morning I had to get up by 5 a.m. to start my physical training, my favorite part of the entire ROTC program. I loved working out and running with my peers. Being so competitive by nature, I thrived on and was actually driven by the challenge of outperforming my fellow cadets. Simply the spirit of running in formation and calling cadences, doing push-ups and sit-ups non-stop, and being part of a team were what I began to live for. But no matter how long or hard I worked out, I was never satisfied with myself. If I didn't devote at least two or three hours each day to exercise and fitness, I felt as if I had betrayed myself. I had to be the best, and I couldn't stop until I was!

Although running helped ease some of my concerns for Daddy, it wasn't enough. And while my Bulimia had been quite dormant for several months, it became more and more intense.

Following the great Southern tradition, practically every person who stopped by to visit Daddy brought food. Cakes, cookies, pies, and Whitman's chocolates were everywhere! It was so incredibly hard for me to resist the temptation! People simply had no idea the battle I fought by the minute to be able to prevent myself from gorging all of Daddy's food at one sitting!

While most people just thought I "ate like a bird," I actually " ate like a pig" in private. When they weren't looking or when everyone was asleep, I would sneak and binge, sometimes for over an hour. Even if there wasn't a lot of food, I could always find some. In fact, my obsession with food was so out of control, I began eating whatever Daddy left on his plate. Perhaps it wouldn't have been so bad to eat off of daddy's plate, but he desperately needed to eat his own food. The chemotherapy had caused him to completely lose his appetite, so he never ate anything. But no one knew that for quite awhile because I had been eating his leftover food without telling anyone.

Once, he asked me why MaMay kept trying to force more food upon him, asking if he wanted second helpings when he hadn't even eaten the first plate full.

"I don't know Daddy," I lied, hating myself with every word.

Over the next year, Daddy's health miraculously improved to the point where we all thought he would survive. His energy returned a bit, and his hair all grew back even more beautiful than it had been before. But Daddy wasn't fooled. By the time he was rehospitalized a few months later, he had completed his will and most funeral arrangements, without our even knowing it.

Daddy was still in the hospital when I had to go on a six-day, ROTC field training exercise in the woods near Redstone Arsenal, Alabama. This was the week all the cadets would be evaluated on the skills we had learned throughout the year. I didn't want to leave Daddy, but he insisted that I go.

It was a very long week. Along with the other cadets, I had to dig my own hole in which to use the bathroom. There was nothing to eat except dehydrated military food. We slept on the ground in a half-shelter while it rained and snowed on our heads, and we had to run around the woods pretending like "the enemy" was there.

After six days of that, I was so excited and thankful to be back, alive and warm again!

As our bus pulled onto the familiar grounds of our college campus, all the cadets began organizing for clean-up detail. It literally took hours to clean the equipment, especially our M16 semi-automatic rifles. Because the "recovery" after an operation was so tedious and time consuming, only the most exceptional cadets were rewarded by being allowed to go home without cleaning weapons and equipment.

On this particular exercise, I had challenged myself to my limit, but I didn't think I had excelled enough to receive that reward.

Nonetheless, my name was called to see the Commander immediately. I was thrilled as I went bouncing into the Commander's office with the biggest smile on my face. But there, I literally bumped into Todd, the guy I had been dating.

I was oblivious as to why my name had actually been called.

"Turn in your weapon and other sensitive items now, Cadet Hulan," the commander said.

I proudly did as I was told, still assuming I had done a really good job on the exercise! Dreaming of some real food and a shower, I enthusiastically climbed into Todd's car. As he began driving towards MaMay's house, his voice quivered as he broke the news to me.

"Leah, your dad is back at MaMay's house, now, but he's not doing well. The doctors say he only has about three months to live."

As we pulled into MaMay's driveway, I could tell by the crowd of cars my entire family was already there.

For the first time, Daddy spoke of death. I couldn't stop the tears or waves of helplessness.

There was absolutely nothing we could do except to try and make Daddy's last days as comfortable as possible.

And we did.

Chapter Nineteen

The Winner Is ...

The death of my father spurred me on to a deeper level of compulsive overeating.

My friends and relatives were never aware of my weakness. In fact, they all thought I was Superhuman with how well I was dealing with my father's death. I even spoke at his funeral because I wanted to share some tender moments Daddy had left me.

In fact, the restraint that I displayed while eating in public was so extreme that most people asked how I could keep from losing weight. But away from scrutiny, I would consume unimaginably large amounts of food, hate myself even more for eating, then go to the bathroom and get rid of it.

That pattern continued throughout the following year, one that was marked with many changes.

Mom sold our farm, against my protests, and moved into Murfreesboro. I had to move with her, of course, but was appreciative to be able to claim the pool house behind her home as my own while I finished my last year in college.

Most of my school work was dedicated to developing my skills as a professional Army officer, because that May, I would be graduating and receiving my commission as a Second Lieutenant. I had already learned that I had been chosen for a regular Army commission in Military Intelligence. Wow! All the hard work had really paid off!

That spring of 1990, my sorority, Delta Zeta, nominated me to be their representative in the Miss Middle Tennessee State University Pageant. I accepted the nomination gladly, even though I truly had no idea what I was getting into.

All I knew was that I had to participate in a judges' interview, perform a talent, present myself in a swimsuit and answer on-stage questions. No big deal, I thought. I had been working-out so intensely that my body was in phenomenal shape. I was graduating with a near perfect 4.0 and felt confident to answer any intelligent question. And, last but not least, clogging could be my talent. I figured I'd just play a tape of "Rocky Top" and dance any step that came to mind. No sweat! It would be great to graduate as Miss MTSU!

"And the winner is ... Leah Hulan!!!" the announcer yelled.

The crowd went wild. I could not believe all that applause was for me. I remember thinking that a lot of people must like the song "Rocky Top!" But then the announcer said that I would represent the university at the Miss Tennessee pageant in June.

I had no idea that I might actually win. Neither did I know that the pageant was a preliminary to the Miss America contest!

But what a glorious feeling to be a winner! For the first time in my life, I felt beautiful!

I was still blustering in my euphoria when I was swept into a back room of the auditorium for the scheduled judges' critique. The purpose of the session is to prepare the new Miss MTSU for competition at Miss Tennessee to enhance her chances of winning the state title.

The judges began the session with a few words of encouragement and congratulations. But then they set out on a ferocious attack.

Among the first things I heard were:

"Don't wear black next time! It makes you look too coarse and too hard!"

"A more flattering dress design is definitely a necessity!"

"You appear to be 'hippy' on stage, and TV will add some more weight to your bulky thighs anyway!"

"You'll need some walking lessons before Miss Tennessee. You walk like you are in the military and a bit pigeon-toed!"

"You had better be pushing away from the table — or not even sitting down to eat — because you need to drop about 15 pounds in the next 8 weeks!"

"Yes, we know you are very muscular, but this isn't the Army. This is Miss Tennessee we are talking about! Your competitors will have phenomenal bodies, so if you are serious about winning, your body will have to be flawless! Especially with that talent of yours — clogging! It's not exactly like being a classical pianist or an opera singer!"

"You could wrap your thighs in cellophane before running."

"Your breasts could use a push-up or something, because a more voluptuous look is the standard."

"Just get all that weight off and remember everything else you've heard us say tonight, and you'll do fine! Good luck!"

The slaughter seemed to go on and on.

As I heard the judges picking me and my body apart, bit by bit, piece by piece, I felt like a pulverized roadkill being ravenously dissected by a flock of vultures eating me for lunch.

I was nearly in tears, as I clutched my trophy and crown in my hands and searched for my sister.

"How did I ever win?" I wondered. "And where did they want me to lose weight and how?"

I only weighed 115 pounds and was already running 3-5 miles daily in ROTC.

"What more could I do without starving myself again?"

I had the answer.

Chapter Twenty

Not One Single Bite

As I began to prepare for the Miss Tennessee contest, I learned more and more about the pageant system.

Until I won Miss MTSU, I had been totally ignorant of "the pageant world, not even knowing there was a difference between the Miss America™ and the Miss USA™ pageants.

At first, it didn't seem to matter. I thought I would have to relinquish the title of Miss MTSU anyway because I was supposed to report for active Army duty immediately after graduation. But my military science professor Lieutenant Colonel Cecil Calloway intervened on his own.

"Leah, you've worked very hard for four years to reach your goal of becoming a lieutenant in the United States Army," he said, after calling me into his office.

"You've been dedicated and devoted to challenging yourself day and night. Even though I'd rather see you in the Army because you have grown into a fine officer, I also feel you have earned the right to compete for the Miss Tennessee title. Good luck!"

This was the deal my professor had arranged. If I won the title of Miss Tennessee, I would not report to active duty until after my reign was over the following year. If I lost, I was to report the very next day to Ft. Huachuca, Arizona for my Military Intelligence Officer Basic Course.

That gave me less than six weeks to prepare for two things — the state pageant which offered over $100,000 in scholarships and/or Army basic training.

The more crazy life seemed to be, the more I pushed myself, especially my body.

I was up before dawn every morning to start my physical fitness routine.

I ran five miles. I rode my bike for over an hour. I'd put on a pair of heavy bluejeans, dive into the pool, and kick for thirty minutes. I'd spend hours reading every newspaper I could find in order to stay updated on the latest current events. I would sit in my room for hours watching old tapes of pageants, memorizing how the winning girls walked. I also relearned how to do my hair and make-up again since it had been years since I had really cared about my appearance.

In between all that, I couldn't neglect my preparation for the Army. I had only a one in forty chance of winning the pageant, so I wasn't placing any bets on myself.

So, all my other waking hours were spent buried in Army manuals, trying to learn every regulation and refresh the knowledge and skills I had learned over the past four years.

I was keeping myself so busy, I flat out forgot all about eating. And if the thought crossed my mind, all I had to do was remember that I would be on television in front of over two million viewers in a swimming suit!

So, while my bulimia disappeared for awhile, anorexia gladly took its place.

I thought that I looked great, having dwindled down to almost 100 pounds. But the fact was that I had denied myself food for so long that I had grown accustomed to not eating. And, if I dared to eat a bite of anything at all, even a banana, I would become furious with myself and work out for an additional hour or two.

One would think that by all the exercising I was doing that I would have become one bulging muscle! But since I was also simultaneously starving myself, my body was burning all the protein from my muscles in order to create fuel. So I simply looked thin and lean, an appearance I relished.

Soon, I was weighing myself ten to fifteen times a day, just to make sure I had not put back on a single ounce.

But no matter how small I became, it still wasn't satisfactory to me. I wanted to be perfect and have the perfect body to match. And unless I was working meticulously towards that goal almost around the clock, I thought I was decreasing my chances of being "validated" as a worthy, good, pretty individual at the Miss Tennessee pageant.

Despite all I had done, I lost.

I came in first runner-up.

So, as all the other contestants were dancing at the post-pageant ball, I was on my way to Arizona for basic officer training.

I felt like I had disappointed everyone.

On the airplane, staring out at the black night, my hair was still swept up in the glamorous, pageant style it had been in on stage only hours before. But gone were all the other signs of glitz and glamour.

Gone were all the adoring fans.

Gone were all my hopes of being recognized as a beautiful, worthy person.

The next day, I stood in my green Army uniform and combat boots, taking orders and shuffling about, acting like and looking like everyone else.

I remember thinking that's all I would ever be, a robot—taking and carrying out orders for someone else's dreams.

My feelings of ugliness and obesity returned.

Where were the cheers as I walked out on stage? Where were the hoots and hollers as I danced? Where was that public acceptance I'd felt that "Leah is okay?"

I needed these things! I needed them to feel special! And now they were gone!

Chapter Twenty-One

Love at First Sight

I had only been at Ft. Huachuca for several days when I saw the most beautiful man that I had ever seen in my entire life!

I was running down the steps of the barracks with a new friend named Randy when I rounded a corner and almost bumped right into another lieutenant.

"Wow!" I said out loud, thinking that he looked like an absolute god!

"Randy, now that is a man I could fall in love with!"

I rented a place to stay at Sierra Carmichael apartments that afternoon, and Randy rented an apartment directly beneath mine. That was great news to me, especially since I didn't have a car.

Settling into my new life was tougher than I had imagined, both in classroom studies and physical training. But I loved it.

I'll never forget my first morning of physical training. With all my working out, I knew that this area was my forte. If I could physically hold my own with the males, especially if I could even outperform them, surely I would earn their respect. I looked at this as my opportunity to dispel the "dumb blonde" jokes I'd heard behind my back since I had arrived.

That morning, there were soldiers everywhere! And suddenly, as the commander welcomed our new unit, all the other soldiers gave us a thunderous round of "Fresh Meat! Fresh Meat! Fresh Meat!"

"What energy and motivation!" I thought. "I'm really going to like this!"

And I did. Even after all the beauty tricks I had learned in the pageant world, I tied my hair back and put away my make-up, letting my blemishes show.

It was during physical training that I once again saw my "dream god!"

He was bending over, leading his own class in calisthenics when I caught him staring at me between his legs! When he saw me looking, I think he blushed!

I thought he looked like a Greek sculpture — chiseled face, rippled abs, and biceps to die for! He was absolutely breath-taking! I could have gawked at him all morning, but my class leader noticed the focus of my attention.

"Hulan!" he barked. "You're here to exercise your body, not your fantasies!"

I blushed then!

I had never in my life simply looked at a guy and fallen in love with him before, but that's how I felt!

But it was several days before I actually met Tom — when I gathered the nerve to knock on his barracks door.

"Come in! It's open," he said before looking up. "What can I do for you?"

Wow! I had acted so impulsively by knocking on his door that I hadn't even thought of a polite excuse for bothering this guy!

I mumbled something about looking for a friend to get a ride back to my apartment. Tom offered to give me a lift himself.

"Perfect!" I thought.

And that was the beginning of the most beautiful relationship I had ever experienced. For the remainder of our six-month military intelligence course, Tom and I were inseparable. He taught me how to ride a motorcycle. I watched all his football games. We played pool and darts, and we worked out at the gym together. We watched college football on Saturdays and pro football on Sundays, always cheering for Tom's favorite Miami Dolphins.

For the first time in my life, I felt truly in love and closer to being fulfilled than I had ever thought possible.

But the sturdy walls around me weren't thick enough to fight off my old demons.

Every time I looked at Tom, I found him even more appealing than the time before. But next to him, I often felt homely and unbecoming. But I desperately wanted him to adore and worship me as I did him!

It seemed the more I had, be it affection, love, pride or whatever, I wanted more.

Soon, I began to dream of competing for the Miss Tennessee title one more time — and my Bulimic binges and purges came back to haunt my new-found peace.

In the meantime, Tom and I made arrangements so that following Army Airborne courses in Georgia, we would be stationed together in Central America.

I graduated from the officer basic course that December, but any pride I felt was lost a few weeks later when I injured my knee at Airborne school, an injury that prevented me from earning my coveted wings.

Feeling like a complete and utter failure because I had not completed the school, I reported to my assignment in Central America with an injured knee and ego and plummeting self-esteem.

At that particular time, Panama was considered a dangerous "hot-spot" assignment. But I would have gone anywhere at that point to be with Tom. I had become so attached to him, perhaps addicted to him, that I thought I simply could not exist without him. I felt as if there was no "Leah" without "Tom."

So, together we blazed into Panama!

Rumors of "Barbie and Ken" echoed throughout the small base. I relished the attention. Tom didn't. He was a very private person and resented being the object of conversation and gossip.

Soon, to nurture my self-esteem, I began putting myself and my own goals above my relationship with Tom. So, when the golden opportunity came knocking at my door to compete for a second chance of becoming Miss America, the lure of recognition was too much to ignore.

If I could compete and win, I might really become that beautiful, powerful stallion of my youthful dreams!

Chapter Twenty-Two

Chasing the Crown

Dazzled by fame and fortune, I was blind to the fact that I already had everything in life that was really important — my career, my health and a loving relationship.

But I threw it all away.

I resigned my regular Army commission, was re-appointed as an officer in the Tennessee Army National Guard and set off for home.

While I cannot speak for the thousands of young, talented women who enter beauty pageants all across America every year, I can say I was caught up in pageants for all the wrong reasons.

As a little girl, I had watched the pageants on TV. The beaded gowns, high heel shoes, puffy hair and make-up were far from the reality of our life on the farm. But I did dream of escaping into the dazzling world of beauty crowns. Perhaps it was those youthful dreams that charmed me as an adult into competing in pageants.

Beyond that, I had always measured my self-worth in the way others "judged" me.

I didn't realize that people engaged in pleasant conversations and discussions with me just for the sake of being friendly. Instead, I thought they were simply testing my knowledge in a certain area, judging my opinion on a certain matter, evaluating my intelligence and expecting to be perfect. That's why I constantly read newspapers, watched CNN and read only non-fiction books and articles.

If I wasn't applying myself physically or academically every second of my life, I felt I was cheating myself — and decreasing my chances of becoming Miss Anything!

So it wasn't long before I had forgotten how to have fun and to relax. Relaxing for me was watching Cross Fire on CNN, memorizing the components of the latest health care reform bill and rehearsing why I agreed or disagreed.

The constant pressure I put myself under fed upon itself.

How could I appear to be perfect on the inside, while all along feeling that I was inferior?

Especially physically!

The "ideal" body that I had created in my mind would be difficult to achieve again. Since I had starved down to less than 100 pounds during my first attempt at winning Miss Tennessee and still didn't win, I assumed that this time I must work more rigidly at achieving physical perfection.

Although cosmetic surgery would have made my journey to perfection a lot easier, for many girls in pageants like myself, cosmetic enhancements were never an option. Not only could I not afford the financial expense of cosmetic surgery, I was also afraid that a new, flattering bust line would prevent me from doing my required push-ups in the national guard. Funny, but true!

Nonetheless, the pressure and stress to look like this "ideal woman" was all-consuming for me.

And the work paid off, at least halfway.

I won the title of Miss Tennessee 1992 — but I lost the Miss America Pageant.

Rather than reaping the rewards and basking in a feeling of complacency after achieving a goal, I immediately focused on another task.

What do you do when you lose the Miss America contest?

You enter the Miss USA™ pageant, of course!

So, I entered the USA pageant system and won the title of Miss Tennessee USA™ 1994. That made me one of the few women to ever compete, back to back, in the two national pageants.

In the meanwhile, Tom had placed his pride on the line for me one last time by asking me to marry him. More than anything, I thought I wanted to be his wife but the timing was wrong, I reasoned.

I still had to prove myself — to myself and to him!

My self-doubt was incredible.

Without winning a national pageant, I wondered what I had accomplished to be worthy of him? What did I have to offer him?

I accepted his marriage proposal, but only with the understanding that my new title of Miss Tennessee USA™ meant I had to stay in the states the full year, while he was stationed in a different country. That meant postponing our wedding a year.

I don't think either one of us were sure our love could stand much more time apart.

For me, the years of pressure to be "pageant thin," as well as some parasitic people who attached themselves to me just because of the Miss Tennessee titles, began to beat me down. I completely lost sight of real life goals, in exchange for the materialistic, short-term rewards.

"Leah," for all practical purposes, ceased to exist as an individual, or even as a person.

I became poisoned by my unquenchable thirst for attention.

And the more attention I received, the more I craved, until my body and mind responded to the constant pressure through intense and incessant Bulimic bouts.

Chapter Twenty-Three

The Chase Goes On

Although Tom had seen some of the warning signs of my bulimia, he was so far away that he didn't see the real and ugly truths that fed my ego and my ambition.

He was one of the many people who assumed my tireless need for acceptance and perfection stemmed from the outside pressure of the pageant world to be thin.

In reality, the only pressures for me to be anything more or less than I already was came from within. I generated all the pressure to be perfect. Pageants had nothing to do with it. They simply became an outlet for my own diseased thinking.

As predicted, my relentless efforts to win a national title — even after promising that each pageant would be the last — was a huge factor in the deterioration of my relationship with Tom.

We were barely hanging on when I embarked on my preparation for the Miss USA™ contest.

To heighten the pressure, if that was possible, I knew this would be the last pageant in which I could ever compete.

I would be 26 years old soon, the maximum age for competition.

Soon, I was competing in a potentially deadly marathon with myself.

I would get up at 4 a.m. and do my "Abs of Steel" workout for 30 minutes. I would then swim two miles, nonstop. I would dry my hair, eat two slices of an apple and drive to the gym. There, I would lay in the tanning bed for thirty minutes. Then I would do the morning aerobics class, followed by 30 minutes on the step machine or the bicycle. Running for about an hour was next on the agenda, followed by twenty minutes in the steam room or sauna. By this time, it was usually time for afternoon aerobics, after which I worked out with free weights for two hours. I would leave the gym around 8 p.m.

Once home, I would watch CNN for an hour, read the paper and then go to bed, just to start the same routine all over again the next morning.

I did all this, as well as finding the time to vomit about 15 times a day — the pressure of being the "ideal" and being thin was simply too great for me to handle without bingeing and purging.

Sometimes, I would surprise myself though and be impressively strong and able to starve for days again, like I used to. But then, I would experience a weak moment and binge once again.

The cycle was the same as usual. The feeling and texture of food as I felt it in my mouth was a heavenly delight. I was so hungry that once I gave in to the temptation of food, I simply could not control myself. I would eat and eat and eat. I could not stop eating! It was such a pleasure to taste sweets and to chew a piece of meat. Yet, within minutes of bingeing, I would become extremely angry and hostile with myself for the indulgence. After all, I had prepared for competition for months and sacrificed time and happiness with Tom in pursuit of this dream!

"How dare you be so pitiful and weak!" I screamed out loud, glaring repulsively at myself in the mirror. "I can't believe you poisoned your body with food! Get rid of it! Get rid of all of it, now!

"You are fat and ugly! You do not deserve to eat! You are wicked! Get rid of it now!"

As I repeated these words, the pugnacious and nasty thoughts became iron fists, relentlessly punching me in the stomach until I heaved and purged my body free of the "toxins."

Sometimes, especially after eating spicy foods and after intense purging, my throat would become raw and bleed from the strain.

God! What a maniac!

I was not intentionally trying to hurt myself or jeopardize my health, but when I would envision being on national TV in my swimsuit, I couldn't help but starve. The image that I saw in the mirror was fat and ugly! Even though at certain times I might temporarily feel pretty or more confident than usual, I still cringed from the thought of competing against all those beautiful girls with their incredible bodies!

After putting my body through such an extreme work-out regimen, I did, temporarily, have an awesome body, one hundred percent pure muscle!

But finally, my body began fighting back.

I began to get sick constantly, catching every virus that meandered by. But I didn't, couldn't, slow down.

It mattered not that my hair had begun to fall out. It mattered not that my teeth were losing their luster. It mattered not that my kidneys bled or that my heart pulsed irregularly on occasions. It mattered not that I isolated myself from my friends and had become a recluse. It mattered not that food had become poison rather than nourishment.

All that mattered and all that was important was maintaining my focus and winning the title of Miss USA™! I had to prove to myself that I could do something right! I just knew that I could! There would be nobody to blame except my own inadequacy as an individual if I didn't capture the title this time! For once in my life, I thought I was in control of my own destiny! I was in the driver's seat. I held the reins in my bare hands! For sure, this time, I would finally be a success!

Two weeks before departing for the Miss USA pageant, I became ill. And although I only weighed 102 pounds, I thought I was still fat. My fever approached 104 degrees and would not break.

Upset by this obstacle to my working-out, I decided that I would work out anyway! Without anyone knowing, crying from the pain, I made myself do sit-ups and push-ups on the floor of my bedroom until I couldn't tolerate the pain anymore.

Down to only one week until competition, everyone started getting nervous about my ability to get well and compete.

To make matters worse, I lost my voice and couldn't even squeak out a sound. I went to several doctors, but nothing was working.

Finally, two days before departure, I went to a very expensive and arrogant throat specialist. He worked his magic on me, loaded me down with medication, charged me a small fortune and sent me "babbling" on my way to Miss USA!

My voice came back, but my fever stayed. I was on strong antibiotics throughout the two long weeks of competition.

In a bitter twist of irony, winning had meant so much to me that my "overkill" physical preparation for the pageant was probably the leading reason why I became ill, preventing me from doing my best.

I didn't win the contest, finishing only as a semi-finalist.

I was utterly distraught. That had been the last pageant I could ever compete in.

What was I going to do now to feel accepted by society and to prove that I was worthy as a person?

Chapter Twenty-Four

Going to the Chapel

I dealt with my disappointment by focusing on my wedding.

I would not be able to get married until after relinquishing my crown in October, but Tom's tour in Panama had been extended until then anyway.

We set the date for November 5, 1994, and I plunged into the planning and organization.

Within weeks, I had almost completed all the arrangements.

We chose a Catholic Church since I was converting to Tom's religion so that we could share our faith together. We both had our initial meetings with a priest in Murfreesboro and also in Panama when I was visiting there. Tom was to wear his Mess Dress Blue Army uniform. I was to wear one of my white pageant dresses with an attached train. The china and silver had been picked out and registered, and the invitations had been planned. The guest list was almost complete, as well as the arrangements for music and the reception.

I was more than eager for the date to finally arrive. I was ready to commence really living and to share my life with the man I loved. I wanted to put my disappointments behind me and move on!

But the days slipped by slowly as I honored all the contracts I had committed to as Miss Tennessee USA™.

And it was one of these commitments that would change a lot of things in my life, forever.

I traveled to a small town to give a speech against drug abuse. Whenever I traveled and had time, I would call old friends who lived in the area, just to stay in touch.

This trip, I called a man I had known and admired for years.

He was a brilliant, self-made man who had worked his way up to become very successful in his field. He had a great wife, wonderful kids, and seemed to have everything. I had the utmost respect for him because he seemed to be able to accomplish absolutely anything he put his mind to, and I wanted to grow and develop along the same track as he had.

When I arrived at the hotel, I called his office. While I usually had dinner with him and his family whenever I came through town, that night he said his wife and children were away on vacation, so we made arrangements to have dinner at a nearby restaurant with a girlfriend of mine whom he also knew.

She came to my hotel before dinner, and we had a couple of glasses of wine before going by his place. Once there, he mixed us some of his favorite margueritas.

I only had one, but when I stood up to go to dinner, I found myself extremely dizzy and almost staggering to the door.

"Whooooah!" I slurred. "I think we better eat back at the hotel restaurant. You both know I don't drink very often, but when I do, I get awful sleepy!"

But he firmly insisted on going to his favorite restaurant.

"I'll take care of you, don't worry!" he said. "We don't get to see you often, Leah, so let me indulge a bit, okay?"

From what I recall, the restaurant was very plush. We ordered appetizers while we waited on the entrees, and he ordered another round of drinks and proposed this toast:

"To Leah, how proud we are of you!"

I hugged him with thanks. He was like a father figure, and I relished his belief in me.

Everything was going great until I ate my salad. It was the first food I'd had all day, and I'd had too much alcohol. I became upset that I was eating anything at all. I thought I had been so good the past several days, basically not eating a single meal.

Perhaps the alcohol had lowered my resistance to the temptation of food. Regardless, I made up my mind to remedy the problem immediately. I stood up to excuse myself from the table, but the room began spinning around and around and around.

I started stumbling.

Suddenly, I felt a strong arm around my waist and heard a familiar voice coax me down a dark corridor. Inside a blurry room, I found myself staring at the porcelain toilet as I heaved uncontrollably, purging the "poison" I thought was causing my hysteria.

The next thing I remember was riding in a car, suddenly needing to vomit again.

Futilely, I attempted to roll down the electric windows. I felt myself get sick in the car and all over myself.

I barely remember being carried out of the car to somewhere.

"Housecleaning," the hotel maid said, walking into the room. "Oh, excuse me, Miss!"

Groggily, I sat up in bed and squinted at the clock.

It was nearly noon! I couldn't believe I had slept that late — I couldn't even remember going to bed!

I laid back down, burying my throbbing head under the covers.

My god! I did not have on a stitch of clothes except my socks!

My head was pounding as I strained to remember the events of the night that led me into such disarray. My throat was dry, and my body felt numb. Nauseated and aching miserably all over, I wanted nothing more than to sleep. But like a bolt of lightening, I remembered I had to give a speech in less than an hour!

Jumping straight up in bed, and once again staring at the clock, I was confused. For one, I could actually see the clock — my eyesight is so bad, I can hardly see anything without help. I must have passed out with my contacts still in my eyes. But how did I get in bed and undressed?

I glanced hurriedly around the room and saw evidence of the night's ordeal laying strewn all about. My shoes were nowhere to be found, but I saw my clothes, including my bra and panties, scattered haphazardly all around the floor.

Looking back at the bed, I noticed makeup smeared all over the previously white pillowcase. And then I saw that my telephone was off the hook, with the receiver tucked under the other pillow, with a phone book balanced on top of it.

"No wonder I didn't get my wake-up call," I muttered.

Stumbling cluelessly to the bathroom, I became nauseous at the sight and smell of vomit on the bathroom floor.

"When did I get sick?"

I showered quickly and began applying my makeup, resigning to allow my hair to dry by itself. I was in no mood or condition to be giving a speech and smiling at people. My head and body still felt like a truck had run over me, but I carefully tried to make myself look presentable. But as I stared at my face in the mirror, strange images from nowhere flew into my mind and dissipated. I attributed this bizarre hallucination to the dizziness that I was still experiencing. I shook my head and continued to fix my face.

Suddenly, the strange images were back like a hot flash, except this time they stayed long enough for me to interpret what I saw.

I was laying on my back in the bed. My head was spinning as I watched a ceiling fan go round and round and round. Then, there was a huge, powerful force on top of me, but I could not see anything. My vision was completely blocked. I tried to speak, but my words were muffled. A pillow was flattening my face! I could taste it! I felt cold air all about me, and was reaching for the covers but could feel nothing. My arms were tingling and my legs felt pinned down.

The images in my mind kept turning and turning! Vibrant colors leaped from out of nowhere. They were so bright and vivid, they hurt my eyes and were burning my skin. Then I saw intense flames and felt them on my body. The scorching sensation slowly moved down my neck then hovered for a long time over my breasts, devouring them with wet, hot kisses. The flames reached out to me like grasping fingers clawing my flesh. My breasts began to burn and sting from the fiery sensation. I tried to break free, but I couldn't get away.

Biting and sucking sensations tormented my tender nipples. The fingers of the fire continued to pinch and slap my helpless breasts, causing me to moan in pain.

Gradually, the fire spread down my chest and across my stomach. I couldn't escape the ferocious fire!

I felt the sizzling force hover above my own private area as if it were blowing hot air between my legs. A few seconds later, I felt drowned by a downpouring of burning, acid rain all inside myself. The sensation totally engulfed me, penetrating my deepest self, burning and stinging incessantly.

I was in Hell! I knew it! Somehow, I had died and gone to Hell without realizing the transition! This was pure, undiluted Hell! And it must be the Devil, himself, attacking me!

The fire continued pillaging my body, scorching every area personal to me then slapping my bare buttocks, repeatedly. I struggled for what seemed like an eternity, until I felt a warm breeze sweep my naked body.

I thought the fire had faded away.

But once again, I felt the burning acid drip all over my stomach and chest again. I wondered how a fire could continue to burn over an already scorched area. But it did, in and out, the fire swept again and again!

Suddenly, back staring in the mirror, I almost screamed:

"It couldn't be! It just could not be true! I thought he was my friend! Oh, God, no!"

I rushed out of the bathroom. Near the bed, I saw a small, crumpled mess on the floor. It was a used condom.

Revolted, I ran to the bathroom, vomiting all the way.

"I hate you!" I screamed at myself. "I hate you! I hate you! Why have you allowed this to happen?"

Then my hands began slapping my face, over and over as I yelled:

"Bad girl! Feel the pain? Feel the pain, bad girl! It is nothing compared to the pain you will suffer from now on! You will never be able to escape now, bad girl! You terrible, terrible bad girl!"

My face was stinging from the incessant slaps, and my lip was bleeding before I stopped hitting myself.

But I wasn't through. I walked over to the refrigerator and quickly ate the stock of goodies.

I stayed closed up in my room the entire day, ordering room service. Like a beast, I ate linguini, hamburgers, broiled chicken, salads, and croissants. I ate five muffins with butter and jelly. I ate a baked potato loaded with sour cream and onions. Dessert was my favorite, and since I couldn't make up my mind which one I wanted, I ordered one of each. I shoved down a piece of key lime pie, cheese cake, apple pie, and German chocolate cake down my throat. Then, I walked straight to the bathroom and rid everything from my stomach into the toilet.

Then I repeated the procedure, ordering room service three more times.

At some point, I collapsed on the floor.

I was awakened by a knock at the door. I looked at the clock. It was after 9 p.m.

Before going to the door, I became aware of the utter mess both the room and I were in. There was food all over the bed and floor. Empty, dirty dishes were scattered all about. My hair was disheveled, falling all in my face. My eyes were almost swollen shut. Blood and make-up streaked my face.

I slowly pulled my body up from the floor, wrapped the large hotel room robe around me and barely opened the door.

It was him. He pushed his way in.

"Hey kiddo! You look like shit!" he said cheerfully. "Have you recovered from last night?"

I was stunned.

"What do you mean?" I asked.

"Well," he said nonchalantly. "I was wondering if all those double drinks I was pouring and ordering for you had had a chance to wear off?"

Feeling really awkward with him in my room and acting as if nothing had happened, I began to doubt my memories. But at that moment, I saw another crumpled up, wad of rubber clinging to the edge of the bed. The other condom.

"Don't patronize me, you son of a bitch!" I screamed. "You violated me! That's against the law, you pervert! You raped me while I was passed out! Admit it!"

He laughed out loud and said:

"Violate you? Not hardly, little girl! You were practically begging for it!"

It was a surreal argument.

I screamed:

"I don't even remember coming back here! How could I have begged you for anything?"

"Calm down," he said, assuredly. "You sure seemed to enjoy it last night!"

Then he started walking toward me.

I ran over to the phone to call the police.

"Just what do you think you are doing young lady?" he whispered, grabbing the phone and smashing it back down on the hook.

Then he grabbed me. I shrugged to avoid his nasty kisses as he held me so tight I could hardly breath. He started rubbing himself against me and quickly darted his hand under my robe, trying to probe me. I started sobbing and kicking as he threw me to the floor.

"No pillow this time, young lady!" he said, throwing himself on top of me. I want you to see exactly everything that you are getting! This way, there will be no doubt how much you truly want me inside you!"

I was dumbfounded.

"Go ahead!" I yelled. "Rape me again, you bastard! But unless you kill me, I will tell everyone, including your wife! I'll tell the police! And I'll tell your boss!"

He began laughing hysterically.

"Leah, Darling!" he continued once again. "If you tell a soul, I'll explain that we shared some cocaine and a bit of acid last night and that you were a willing and enthusiastic partner.

"When are you going to wake up from Never-Never land and realize how you got so drunk so fast! Did you think it was merely the alcohol, little girl? You are even more naive than I had imagined! And all along part of the turn-on was thinking that you were playing a game with me!

"Anyway, believe me, little priss! If you mention any of this to anyone, I'll deny everything and get a drug test on you. It'll prove that you ingested some drugs last night. That should be quite enough for you to lose your so smug 'top secret clearance' in the military and make a lot of headlines!

"I can see it now. 'Miss Tennessee arrested for using cocaine and attacking a man that she invited into her own room!' You have no case, Leah! You can't tell anybody, so, shut up!"

He licked my face and my lips one more time before he got up and pushed one of his boots firmly down on my chest."

Remember what I said, Leah! You have no case!"

Then he wheeled around and left.

Chapter Twenty-Five

Falling Off the Wall

I was trapped inside a world of ugliness.

I was so ashamed of my mistakes. And I had made so many of them for so long. Now, I was at the bottom.

And the nightmares from my past followed me down.

I began to feel lost, and for once, I no longer had the strength to find a new direction or new route to escape.

And I couldn't tell anyone. If I did, I thought I would lose their love. Even my body let me down.

From almost constant binges and purges, my kidneys had begun to bleed, and I was having more and more of my "mini heart attacks." My hair began to fall out in clumps, to the point that I had to wear a hair piece.

I isolated myself, and lied to be able to be alone.

Tom, who had already lost faith in me and our future together, stopped questioning me about my negligence in calling or writing. While I would promise my undying love and dream out loud with him about our soon-to-be life together, I was really always looking for new options to escape, from everything.

Even after I admitted that I had an uncompromising problem and went into counseling, the struggle to ameliorate myself became more difficult.

Soon, I surrendered to the pressure, quit going to counseling, and intensified my bingeing and purging.

Although I wanted help, and knew that I needed help, my lack of finances gave me an excuse to acquiesce, without continuing to search for solutions to my problems and help for my disease.

But I rationalized that I could get well on my own, merely by trying harder to stay busy and not think about food. But how do you escape an obsession?

I sabotaged myself.

I cancelled the wedding, breaking my engagement to Tom.

Chapter Twenty-Six

Two Months, That's All

I went to the doctor.

After my physical exam, he asked if it would be all right to bring in a psychiatrist for our consultation. I made no objection.

For several long and uncomfortable minutes, the three of us sat in a silent circle in his office. It seemed as if no one knew what to say or where to begin.

Then, looking me directly in the eye and without any further hesitation, my doctor resolutely stated his assessment.

"Leah, " he began. "Please listen to me with your undivided attention and an open mind for once, okay?

"Are you ready and willing to listen to what I have to say?"

I nodded.

"Yes, sir. I want to know what is wrong with me, and I want to know how to finally get well!"

Although I was aware that my physical condition was rapidly deteriorating after years of constant maltreatment, I was not expecting nor prepared for the words that came out of my doctor's mouth.

"Leah, your body has begun to show signs of organ failure. Your condition could be considered life-threatening. Even though I don't think the damage is irreparable, if you do not stop bingeing and purging right now, you could very well be dead in two months.

"Two months, Leah! You could be dead within two months unless you stop this destructive behavior!"

As I listened, I drifted off into my own little world.

I was conscious of him still lecturing me, but my mind seemed to float out of my body into a more peaceful place. I stared out the window in his office, concentrating on the brilliance of the sunlight as it danced across the windshields of passing cars. The reflections cast rays of vivid colors shimmering in all directions. The wind was blowing hard, forcing leaves to tumble from the branches of the trees and fall to the ground.

My daze was abruptly interrupted by my doctor grasping my shoulders with his hands.

"Leah, are you listening to me? We are going to do everything we can to help you, but you must begin to help yourself! We cannot win this battle without your complete support and dedication!"

I could only whisper.

"I have tried. I have tried, again and again, to get better. It scares me to hear your words, and they make me want to close my eyes and escape into another world. I'm afraid to keep trying because I just don't believe that anything will work. I don't want to raise my hopes of getting better one more time, only to be disappointed again!

"Every time I suffer another defeat, I react by getting even more depressed and sick. Please don't promise that you can help me and uselessly raise my hopes again! I have tried everything! I simply do not know what to do next."

My doctor made a few phone calls, and miraculously, I was granted admission to a psychiatric hospital in Nashville.

I was ecstatic, filled with an invigorated spirit that I would finally be receiving in-patient, professional help. I called and took a leave from the national guard. I canceled all my obligations for the following six weeks. Then I spent the entire weekend preparing to enter the hospital the following Monday. Even though the hospital didn't specialize in merely eating disorders, I would be living in a very controlled environment, participating in individual and group therapy, as well as being visited by special doctors and psychologists daily.

I was very nervous and a bit apprehensive, but I knew that I had to aggressively attack my ailment before it was too late!

But it wasn't to be.

That Sunday night, my doctor called. The hospital had retracted the offer to admit me because of my extremely poor physical condition. The doctors there had told him they didn't have the medical equipment nor the staff to handle my degree of physical damage, and that they did not want to be liable.

I cannot describe the blow.

Why had I let them get my hopes up?

I ate myself into oblivion and spent the remainder of the evening puking my brains out.

"God, help me!" I sobbed, sitting on the floor in a corner of the kitchen, rocking myself back and forth. "Help me, please!

"I can't do it any longer! I'm sinking, faster and faster! Please help me!"

God must have heard me. It just took me a while to recognize it.

Chapter Twenty-Seven

No Going Back

I suppose I did it to punish myself.

Tom had written me a letter, explaining he was heading back to Ft. Huachuca, Arizona for an advanced military intelligence course. He was returning to the place we had met and fallen in love.

On his way there, he had written that he would be stopping in Lexington, Kentucky for a few days to see his old fraternity friends.

Although I had started dating a wonderful guy named Richard, once I learned that Tom would be a state away from me soon, I became obsessed with winning his love back.

I knew it would be uphill.

Tom had already told me over the phone that it was over between us, and that he had been dating someone else. But I reasoned that he was sending me conflicting signals because he said he wasn't in love with the girl, and he had asked me to attend his college homecoming in Lexington with him.

Determined to make things right between us, I packed my bags and planned to stay with him for his entire visit. Thoughts of a reconciliation began to swim around in my head, blocking all rational thought. I simply could not bear the thought of Tom being in love with anyone else, even though I had fallen for Richard.

So, memories of Tom began to haunt me, all the tender, magical moments that we had shared in Arizona. I began to fool myself into reminiscing about how perfect things had been with Tom when we were in love. My every thought began to focus on how I could make Tom give me one more chance. I just knew that if I could bury myself into recreating the love we used to know, then I could forget about all my problems and find happiness.

All in all, I shifted my attention to this challenging mission in order to prevent myself from concentrating on the real issues — I was an extremely co-dependent person, looking for happiness and love through others and not in myself. I was emotionally unstable, still detesting and mentally abusing myself for allowing myself to be raped once again. I was running from my relationship with Richard because he had so much power over me already; I was afraid that he would soon break my heart. And I was into my disease so far over my head, I was drowning in my own pity.

This was the girl who got into her car and drove to Kentucky — even though Tom hadn't even called to confirm the homecoming date.

As soon as I found a hotel room in Lexington, I called the apartment of Tom's friends.

Tom, acting surprised, answered the phone.

"I don't mean to be rude, Leah," he said, when I told him where I was. "But, who invited you?"

My excitement caught in my throat.

"What do you mean?" I asked. "I just assumed everything was on and that you couldn't get a call through from Panama, so I figured I would just surprise you and show you how much I love you by being here."

Tom explained that he didn't know I was coming in and had already made arrangements with his college friends that night. He said it would only be a bunch of guys and that it really wasn't the opportune time for us to see each other for the first time in so long. He promised he would get a ride to my hotel the next morning and we could talk. And that was it. He hung up.

I had traveled for four hours anxiously awaiting to see my perceived "soul-mate" and the man whom I had recently been engaged to, and he just said he'd see me tomorrow sometime! I was terribly hurt, but I eagerly accepted what he said, and began dreaming about the next day.

That night in the hotel room, I worked out incessantly and didn't eat a bite. I wanted to look thin and great for Tom the next day.

The next morning came and went without hearing a word from Tom until late afternoon. He said he had partied so late, he had slept most of the day away. Then he gave me directions to the apartment where he was, and said he'd see me in a while.

Quickly, I drove to the designated place, forgetting my despair at having impatiently waited all day for his call.

Regardless, I charged up the apartment stairs hoping for a warm welcome. I knocked on the door and heard someone say to come on in.

I did, but Tom never changed his prone position on the couch. He and several of his friends were laying around, watching TV and nursing their hang-overs. No one said hello. No one offered me a seat. No one did anything. I tried to be polite and say a few words to Tom, yet, it was an extremely awkward situation. Tom said he would call me later, making excuses that his friends had not seen him in a long time, and that he felt obligated to spend some time with them.

I wanted to ask, "What about me?"

Instead, I bought a bottle of cheap wine, and I went back to my hotel. And waited.

The hours slowly crept by. Eight o'clock. Nine o'clock. Ten o'clock. Midnight. I opened the bottle of wine and began to sip on it myself. I started calling his friend's apartment, every ten minutes, until I finished off the wine. At three o'clock in the morning, I called the number one more time and a raspy voice answered.

I asked for Tom, and the guy said that Tom was passed out on the floor and he couldn't wake him up.

I hung up the phone feeling totally humiliated, rejected and alone. With nothing else to do, I went outside in the cold rain and ran and ran and ran.

I did not want to admit that Tom was over me.

Later that morning, Tom called back and I picked him up. We went back to my hotel room.

He didn't have much to say. I gave him a few presents that I had for him, but he was more impressed with an old movie on TV. Finally, we went to dinner.

"Leah, I don't love you anymore," he said flatly. "I'm in love with someone else. In fact, the reason why you couldn't reach me before I left Panama was because I was with her. She also traveled here with me but has gone on to her home in Kansas to pick up her little girl."

I was devastated and mortally wounded. How could he have fallen in love with someone else so quickly? How could he have so cruelly allowed me to stay three long days and long nights in a hotel by myself, dreaming of a reconciliation, while he was out drinking with his friends and knowing he was in love with someone else all along?

I blamed him, not realizing I had put myself in the perfect place for punishment.

I immediately packed my bags and left, driving over 110 miles an hour along the Bluegrass Parkway, all the way home.

I hugged Richard, knowing how patient and wonderful he had been. But how could I have been so sneaky? How could I have so easily jeopardized our relationship — which had been honest until that time — over someone who no longer gave a hoot about me?

These were the questions I asked myself every moment of the next several days. I became so depressed over my disrespect for Richard's feelings and my humiliation in Lexington, I found the old bottle of Prozac my doctor had described and started taking them again.

I had to pull myself out of this pit because as the reigning Miss Tennessee USA™, I was supposed to be on stage to present my crown to the new winner within a matter of days.

Reluctantly, I began to pack my clothes for the pageant. I would leave that night for Chattanooga, and spend the next several days in rehearsals for the pageant. I was already apprehensive about giving up my crown because I did not want to face any of my pageant friends in my state of mind — or body.

While I hadn't thrown up in over eight days, that was only because I hadn't had a single bite to eat in eight days. And that, plus the double doses of Prozac I'd been taking since returning from Kentucky, were beginning to affect my nerves. I would really have to do an Oscar winning performance to conceal my condition when I walked on stage.

I began to pace the floor, worrying. The more I thought about all those people looking at me and all the girls vying for my crown, the faster I paced the floor. Frantically I began to cry.

"I can't do this anymore! I quit! I cannot play this game any longer! I'm so unhappy, and I'm so tired of running! I don't want to go to Chattanooga tonight! I'll just disappoint everyone if they see me! I simply cannot smile! I can't do it! I can't do it! I can't smile and pretend anymore. I am in so much pain!"

In a daze, I called Tom's mother whom he was supposed to be visiting for a couple of days. He wasn't there. He had gone to be with his new girlfriend.

I savagely gorged down six bowls of cereal and seven honey-roasted chicken breasts. After immediately throwing them up, I returned to the kitchen and found a loaf of homemade sourdough bread that I covered with cream cheese and strawberry jelly. Without even slicing it, I ate the entire loaf. Still not enough to smother my self-hatred, I ate a whole gallon of peanut butter cookie dough ice cream.

Even though I was about to burst, I was thankful that I had eaten all the ice cream because it facilitated my purge. Dairy products were gentle on my throat. They coated my esophagus, protecting it from the burning stomach acids. But I was still having great difficulty ridding myself of the thick, doughy bread, and was having to strain tremendously.

After painfully purging the loaf of bread and remnants of chicken breasts for over an hour, my throat was bleeding unusually bad and my heart was racing uncontrollably.

"Why do I do these things to myself?" I screamed. "I can't stand this anymore. I am going to escape this terror once and for all. Tom hates me, and why do I care? I have Richard now. So why, Leah, do you do the stupid things that you do? Why can't you control your feelings and your actions?"

I had the urge to hurt myself. Other than the one time I had slapped myself, I had never felt like that before.

Remembering that the therapist told me if I should ever feel like hurting myself after using Prozac, I needed to call the hot line immediately.

I couldn't find the number.

Then I tried to call my mother at her boyfriend's house. No one answered.

Then I decided I would call my daddy. He had been dead five years, but I called his old number anyway. There was no answer.

Finally, I called my younger sister Kara. She was able to calm my hysteria by being firm and by keeping me on the phone for a long time. I probably would have talked to her even longer, but there was a loud knock at the front door. I hung up the phone

I looked out the window and didn't see anyone. Yet, the knock echoed loudly in my ears once again, so I went to the door and opened it, coming face to face with a very large man in a trench coat.

"Are you ready to go?" he asked, in a matter-of-fact manner.

"Go where?" I replied. "Who are you?"

The big man repeated his question one more time as he stepped into the house, asking:

"Are you ready to go home with me?"

"Look, mister, I don't know who you are, but you must have me confused with someone else," I said. "I'm not going anywhere with you!"

As I tried to shove him with the door, he stopped it with his body.

"Leah, I've come to take you where you belong. I am the Devil, and you are going with me to Hell!"

Chapter Twenty-Eight

A Rifle, A Bible,
A Corn Field

I was scared to death as I heard this life-like figure say these words.

I couldn't believe what I had just heard or what I was still seeing. But I didn't waste time second guessing myself.

I quickly turned on my heels, fled into the bedroom, I locked the door and grabbed a rifle out of the closet. Then I got my Bible, and hid in a corner, repeating the Lord's prayer. I heard the man pounding on the door, so I prayed faster and faster.

The Devil easily broke through the door and darted into the dark room. I could hear him breathing heavily and whispering that I could not escape this time. I crawled under the bed, slid past him on the other side, and sprang to my feet. I ran outside as fast as I could. I didn't know where I was going. All I knew was that the Devil was close on my heels!

In the meanwhile, Mom and her boyfriend had come home to cook dinner. She was surprised to see my car still parked in the garage, since I should already have left for the beauty pageant in Chattanooga. But then she went into the bedroom.

She was so startled by what she saw, that she screamed for her boyfriend. There, in the corner of the room, lay the rifle, the Bible and a blanket.

She and her boyfriend searched the house and yard. Finding no trace of me, Mom called the police.

I ran until I was too tired to move. The moon was full, and I sat down on the cold, wet ground, hugging my knees to keep warm. I had no concept of time, or reality as I sat there hoping the Devil could not touch me since I was out in the open, protected by God's light. But as the night became cloudier, I feared the clouds would surround the moon and block God's light from protecting me!

I heard a thundering sound of loud footsteps.

I heard my name echoing repeatedly in my ears.

"He found me!" I thought. "The Devil has found me! I don't want to go to Hell! Please don't take me!"

I got up and started running. But I was soon surrounded by a lot of dark figures, all calling out my name. Then I felt a strong grip on my shoulders. I screamed, struggling with my attackers.

Then I opened my eyes.

"Leah, it's Randy," the young man said. "Remember me? I'm with the sheriff's department. You are safe now. You're going to be fine. Just relax. You're safe."

I stopped fighting the deputies, slowly coming back to reality as they walked me out of the corn field. I had no idea what I was doing in a field, where the field was, how I got there, why I was wet and freezing, or why the police were with me.

Back at the house, sitting on the floor and rocking myself back and forth, I tried to explain to my mom and the deputies what had happened.

As I spoke, I realized how ridiculous all the events must have seemed to everyone but me, so I withdrew into my embarrassment. I didn't want to explain anything else. What use was it?

Chapter Twenty-Nine

A Breath of Hope

My night in the corn field left no doubt in my family's mind that I was truly sick.

They could no longer allow me to masquerade my sickness behind lies of well-being and smiles of happiness. This time, they had to listen as I shared with the counselor the many horrendous truths which I had been concealing.

It was absolutely clear to my family and to me that there were only three choices for me now — insanity, death, or recovery.

I was admitted to Mountain View Recovery Center in East Tennessee.

It was a different world.

All bathrooms were locked at all times, and I had to be accompanied by a nurse whenever I needed to use the facilities. Because I tried at first to hide some of my food and later flush it down the toilet, I had to use the bathroom with the door wide open, and then allow the nurse to do all the flushing. After several weeks, I regained my flushing privileges, yet I still had to be observed while I was "taking care of business."

I knew this observation was necessary since I kept having compulsions to purge every time I set foot into a bathroom, but it surely was humiliating. Thankfully, the day before my discharge, I finally earned the honor of going to the bathroom all by myself. I had never realized the luxury of privacy on the toilet before then.

In treatment, radios, TVs, personal magazines or books, sharp objects, food, candy or gum, alcohol-based mouthwash and any type of clothing advertising alcohol, drugs, food, or exercise were all prohibited.

The idea in treatment was to break me down, ridding me of all my old and unhealthy thinking and behavior patterns, and then to reconstruct me upon a new and strong foundation comprised of healthy patterns of living.

One of the most difficult aspects of this for me was that I was not allowed to work-out at all. Not one push-up, not one sit-up, not one leg-lift. Granted, I was guilty of purging in the past through compulsive exercise, yet I wasn't asking to go out and run 10 miles — I just wanted to do a few hundred push-ups and sit-ups at night! Of course the answer was no, but I didn't understand why until I became more stable.

Until I had achieved a certain level of recovery and a certain period of abstinence, my mind would not have been able to allow my body to exercise moderately. The exercising would have trapped me into that same distorted way of thinking that led me into my compulsive routine.

I had to learn to eat and feel comfortable with eating, without my mind believing I had "earned the right to eat" through excessive exercise.

I had to develop the ability to do all things moderately.

It took a long time, and I'm still learning after coming out of the in-patient treatment center.

Now, I am able to enjoy a healthy amount of exercise. The difference is my attitude and the reason why I exercise. Before, I exercised because I felt fat and unworthy to eat unless I had spent all day at the gym or had run at least six or eight miles. I also compulsively exercised so I wouldn't have to think about anything else. Now, I exercise for enjoyment rather than for punishment and I have some of my best "talks with myself" instead of escaping from thinking about anything.

Although I developed a strong foundation for recovery at Mountain View and had stabilized physically and mentally, the entire staff recommended further medical care within a controlled environment. The facility they felt could best respond to my needs was in Tampa, Florida. At first, I was very reluctant to go. Not only did I not have any more money — I had sold everything I owned to get into Mountain View — but also I suppose I had thought that I could waltz into treatment and waltz out a month later, all cured.

But with a progressive disease such as Bulimia, this was not the case. While I had made tremendous progress in facing and decapitating the old demons that were driving me, I was still having a difficult time eating without feeling evil or fat. In fact, in treatment I had tried every way possible to hide my food, exercise and purge. But every new trick I tried, the staff called my bluffs. They really knew what they were doing, and did not let me sneak anything past them. Of course at the time, this infuriated me and I hated everyone. But as I became healthier and more stable, and as I relinquished my "control" over to a Higher Power, I realized that they were saving my life.

I finally agreed to continue therapy in Florida.

It was more like a halfway house than a hospital. But the environment was controlled. I lived with eight other girls who were suffering from anorexia or bulimia, and we alone were responsible for our food and our meals.

I had to weigh and measure all my food by the specific amounts that the nutritionist had designated for me. Then, before I could eat my meal, I had to have another patient check and ensure that I didn't measure too much or too little. My meal plan again was sugar free, caffeine free, high fiber and low fat, which meant that I did have about three servings of fat per day incorporated into the plan. I struggled daily with the "fats" because I did not want to eat them. Even though each fat was only a little serving of salad dressing, butter, or sour cream, my mind tortured me that this small portion of fat would make me gain weight. Constantly, I had to reflect upon everything that I had already learned in treatment to be able to eat my fats without feeling guilty. I had to trust the system and allow it to work for me.

At both treatment centers, each day began with a morning meditation. I used this time to set daily goals and affirmations for myself. These goals usually were quite small even though they were very significant in my recovery. For example, often my affirmations were "I am an honest person" or "My life is a blessed gift from God" or even "I am okay with progress and do not require perfection."

Some of my goals included not manipulating my meal plan by choosing certain foods over others because I knew they had fewer calories, making "dishonesty lists," not to exercise in my room or in the shower, and to allow myself to feel so I could heal. During the pandemonium of each day, I would take a mental time-out and reflect upon the goal and affirmation that I had set for that day. This helped me to stay very focused on recovery.

After morning meditations, I participated in "Gentle Breakfast." That's where there was no talking or laughing, loud music or TV. It was a time to establish a serious respect for food. I often prayed during this time, and actually thought about food being nutrition, as opposed to poison, for my body and mind. I noticed when I took the time to eat slowly and to put eating in its proper perspective in my life, my food obsession began to fade. Also, because there was no talking or TV, I had to concentrate exclusively on eating. I couldn't transfer my previously insane and bad feelings regarding food onto something else. I found that by confronting my fear of food in this manner, the food lost much of the power that it had over me.

Most of the remainder of the days in treatment were filled with various group and individual therapy sessions. Group therapy worked like magic in forcing me to open up and put all my demons and secrets and fears out on the table for everyone to see.

At first, because I had blocked myself from feeling anything for so long in order to avoid the pain, I shared my secrets without expressing any emotion and told my story in the third person, as if the traumas had all happened to someone other than myself. Yet, as I continued to share my pain, as well as to listen to the pain of others, the barriers that I had constructed began to fall.

Block by block, and piece by piece, the wall that shielded me from the world — but also imprisoned me within my sickness — came tumbling painfully down. I never knew I had it in me to be so expressive and so full of emotion until then.

It was a truly painful experience to see myself clearly. I had to question things I had always accepted as the truth, to accept certain consequences and to challenge certain authority. But the pain was necessary to fortify my recovery.

In group therapy, although the other patients each had different problems and various situations, I could relate to each and every one of them in that I'm an addict. Whether someone is an alcoholic, a drug addict, a sex and love addict, or a food addict, it's all the same: An addict is an addict is an addict.

Before commencing treatment, I thought I was alone in my suffering and alone in my pity. But I've learned that I am not so unique after all. In fact, in just dealing with eating disorders, I have read that there are over 40 million people suffering from them today. If anything, this statistic, as well as group therapy, has shown me that I certainly should not feel alone anymore in my struggle and in my powerlessness over food.

In both treatment centers I would get up earlier than was required so I could have some private, personal time to myself. I had grown accustomed to my isolation, and it was stressful to constantly be in the companionship of others. To help alleviate this stress, I coveted any solitude that I could find so I could pray and write in my journal. But because getting in touch with my feelings was a very new concept for me, sometimes the process was overwhelming.

I found that if I kept a daily journal, including my thoughts and feelings as they occurred, it helped me to see and to understand my progress better.

Often, I wrote letters to the people who had hurt me so I could be honest and release my pent up feelings of hatred and anger. Although I never had any intention of actually mailing these letters, simply the therapeutic significance in finally releasing my ill feelings was absolutely invaluable.

Some things hurt more than others. As much as I had adored my father, I began to question why he had never noticed my pain and why, if he felt my step-father was mistreating us, did he take us back home every week-end? To see my perceived perfect father as human, and less than perfect, robbed me of the comforting way I had always believed him to be. Also, even though my mother and I are best friends now, through regressing into my past, I found that I had some bottled up anger towards her for marrying my step-father and for allowing him to make me so unhappy all those years.

Chapter Thirty

An Open Letter

Dear God,

I am learning to trust your guidance, even though I still have my own ideas how I want to live my life. Allow me to share those ideas with you and then let me understand your will for me. In the long run, I hope and pray that it will be your will, and not mine, that will be done.

As I wrote this book, I realized from my own experience that nothing I say or do will change someone else. Even if one is open to changing and open to accepting new ideas, unless that person chooses to change, not much progress can be made. So my goal in writing this book wasn't to try and change all the people suffering from eating disorders; my goal was simply to share the events that fed my disease, and then to share the events that led to my recovery.

While I hope that my story will offer some help and perhaps some comfort to those who are sick and to provide families a degree of understanding about the danger surrounding eating disorders, the bottom line is that I am sharing with others in order to help myself.

In order to reinforce and to keep my recovery, I must continuously give it away. Some may think this is selfish. Granted, whatever I do now, I am doing because I choose to do so. If nothing more, I hope one can read my book and realize more clearly all those things in life that are so often taken for granted such as health and sanity.

Regardless of the problems that we face in life, a low self-esteem is likely to exaggerate them. For years I believed that all my problems would disappear if I could achieve self-esteem through losing more and more weight and consequently earning everyone's acceptance of me. What I lost sight of was that no one's acceptance of me can grant me this. Self-esteem must come from within. Therefore, when I stopped living a dishonest life in my addiction, I was more able to accept myself, faults and all. Also, I learned that everything doesn't have to be black or white, or all or nothing. Really believing this, I was able to accept myself and my progress and not expect perfection all the time. I employ this concept daily in my abstinence.

For example, upon my return from treatment, I felt so confident, I didn't think I would ever have a weak moment with food again. But as soon as I stepped foot inside my grandmother's house at Christmas, smelling all the homemade cookies and desserts, my mouth watered and I became obsessed with sneaking just one cookie. I had learned in treatment to reach out for help when I experienced a compulsion such as this. However, I did not want my family to think I was already having problems the day after I returned from treatment, so I did not ask for help even though it would have been readily available. Also, as I slipped into my old way of thinking, I knew if I asked for help, it would be provided and then I wouldn't be able to eat that cookie.

So, against my own will, as everyone became busy with decorating the house, I stole an entire cookie tin and went into the bathroom. There, I stuffed about 50 cookies into my mouth, even though I had only given myself permission for one. Immediately, I purged myself of the sweets. Sugar, as well as caffeine, were never to have been part of my meal plan again, and here, upon my first visit home, I gave into the temptation of my sweet tooth and my disease.

But the real progress showed through in how I handled my relapse.

Instead of trying to starve myself for days or exercise for hours to make up for the binge and to punish myself for the weakness, I confessed to my mom what I had done. And two hours later at mealtime, I made myself get right back on track with my meal plan, even though I wasn't exactly hungry. Thus, I focused on the progress I had made and did not dwell on my imperfection.

Since I have been in recovery, it's amazing how much love I am now able to give others. Before, when I was so deep into my addictions, I hated myself and thus was incapable of giving and sharing love with others.

For the first time in years, I am actually rejoicing in my day-to-day life, as opposed to merely existing until the next binge or next exciting adventure. Even little things are exciting opportunities for adventure.

I am again with my grandmother, MaMay. I still don't trust myself enough to live alone with food in the house. But now I realize how I overlooked many of the blessings and the joys of living with her, such as baking homemade sourdough bread together or watching Perry Mason Mysteries after our meal. I'm also proud to help her in small ways such as fixing her hair in the mornings, taking her on her errands and to church, and by saving her steps out to the storeroom or anywhere else.

Actually, just sitting and talking with her seems like a luxury now. I've realized that life is very precious and often too short.

I've learned to accept that I am a victim of compulsive behavior in almost everything that I do. Compulsively, I set out to accomplish tasks, compulsively I shop, and compulsively I love.

For alcoholics or gamblers, perhaps they can get better by setting rigid rules such as "Don't Drink!" or "Don't Gamble!" But that obviously that doesn't work when you are addicted to food. That's why I've learned not to set rules for myself, but to employ healthy guidelines.

I am now on a high fiber, low-fat meal plan which enables me to eat four times a day. I eat more food than I have ever eaten and I eat without purging and without feeling guilty about it.

It's amazing, but the balance of nutrients, as well as the absence of sugar and caffeine, have actually caused me to lose fat and appear to be thinner than I was when I was purging through vomiting and exercise!

Isn't that a kick in the rear?

Chapter Thirty-One

Life Over Death

Although I was born with the power to make choices, I never realized it until I began my recovery.

Having been programmed and shaped most of my life by my past experiences, I had chosen a living death as opposed to rejoicing in life. I had become a victim of my environment , as well as my past, and had not known that I had a choice not to live that way. My thinking had indeed become distorted, making it even more difficult to make healthy choices for myself.

Now, I have the power to choose. And even though I am still powerless over food, I have been empowered in a unique way in knowing that it is up to me to choose how I cope with that powerlessness.

For me, I have found strength in turning my disease over to God. I had to let go before I could receive anything in return. I've had to stop using food for my only sources of gratification.

Life in itself is gratifying.

Probably the most fundamental part of my recovery was my recognition that in order to change my behavior, I first had to change my thinking.

I learned that my actions, habits and behavior are generally determined by what I think and by how I feel. Thus, my behavior will change naturally and spontaneously when my thinking changes first.

147

Before my recovery, I thought I had to starve myself or purge every time I ate because I thought I was fat and needed everyone to simply adore me. Now, although I'm by no means as thin as I was during pageant competitions, I no longer feel the intense need to lose weight. I am learning to love and accept myself for who I am on the inside as opposed to how I appear on the outside.

I frequently say now, "Leah Hulan is not about her body. Leah Hulan is much, much more than merely a surface existence!"

I don't feel the need to return to my old behavior of purging even though I have gained a few pounds, because I have a new frame of mind; I have changed my way of thinking. I no longer feel fat or "bad" just because I ate a healthy meal. Thus, I can also accept myself and my physical imperfections now because I no longer have a need to feel inferior or unworthy. By changing my thinking, I am successfully changing my behavior.

I have evolved from a dishonest, self-hating person suffering from a raging disease into an honest, self-loving person learning to live with a controllable disease.

I wallowed in misery for years because I could not figure out how to rid myself of my self-hatred, my perfectionism, and my discomfort regarding my weight. I wanted to exchange these nasty, unhealthy, enslaving feelings for new feelings of self- love, self-acceptance, and freedom. Yet again, for years, I simply did not know how.

As an addict and compulsive person, I had tried to change my feelings and the way I regarded food and myself through exhibiting greater and greater amounts of control over anything. It was important for me to feel like I had some type of control over something since I had been basically robbed of control most of my life. On the surface, even though my disease only granted me control over my food, below the surface, it allowed me to control my pain. My bulimia gave me the power to reward myself or punish myself through the complete restriction of food or immense overeating.

Consequently, by focusing on these problems, I did not have to deal with the real problems, such as low self-esteem, physical abuse, emotional abuse, and sexual abuse.

I had been living one huge lie all my life.

Chapter Thirty-Two

Facing Myself

*"As I walk with God, I can stop running.
As I stop running, I can face myself."*

It was only after I began treatment and became honest with myself and others about all my deceptions in the past, that I was finally able to move forward out of my denial.

It had been my "unwillingness" to see myself as I truly was that had kept me locked up in chaos for so long. I had incorrectly thought that I was protecting myself from the brutality of the real world. However, most of the brutal, injustice of the world that I had perceived, had been exaggerated in my mind. In retrospect, it would have been less painful to confront life's obstacles one at a time as each misfortune was hurled my way, instead of allowing them all to dwell together in the nooks and crannies of my mind. The longer the misfortunes were hidden from discovery, the more they fermented and gathered potency. When they finally became too toxic for my mind to confine, unexpectedly they seeped out, smearing my mask of serenity and poisoning my ill-fated happiness.

Granted, I had been a victim of all types of abuse and had reason to want to conceal their ugly humiliations. But the fantasy world in which

I hid was more dangerous than the very demons from which I was hiding. The reason was that I could never actually find the same degree of happiness and complacency that I pretended existed in my world of make-believe. Therefore, no matter how hard I tried, I could never achieve the ideal perfection of which I dreamed.

Distorted reasoning and irrational thinking began to dictate my survival. I consistently was at war with myself. I wanted to be independent, yet I also wanted someone to take care of me. I was hungry, yet I did not want to eat. Part of me said eat everything you can get your hands on, while another part said don't eat a bite for weeks! Thus, the war raged on, all along blinding my ability to see myself as I was — sick!

But as I surrendered my will over to God, the battleground miraculously cleared itself of all the smoke, and I could see myself clearly.

Now, as I look back over the years of this insanity, I honestly can not understand how I allowed my disease to progress so far without finding help sooner. In fact, even as I reflect upon my "successes," such as my education, my army commission, and even pageants, I am baffled by where I found the time and the energy to do so well. After all, before I began treatment, I cannot remember a single day in the past dozen years that I had known complete sanity.

Lots of times, my accomplishments would convince me that I certainly couldn't be that sick after all. For example, after starving for several months for the Miss USA Pageant™, I had lost so much weight in an unhealthy manner that I had begun to lose my hair and bleed occasionally from the rectum. But I was able to overlook my deteriorating health because all I could see was how beautiful I thought I looked with my hip bones protruding! I also reasoned that if I were really sick, my family would be more concerned and offer me some help. Yet, as a result of my manipulation, denial, lying and bargaining, combined with my outward ability to operate efficiently in certain other areas of my life, the insanity that twisted my daily existence continued undetected until it was almost too late.

However, when I became honest for a change, most of the insanity calmed down to a point where I could deal with it better. Suddenly, I could see myself as a woman and not a child anymore. I didn't have to pretend to be someone whom I was not because as an honest person, I learned to love and like myself for who I am.

Although I still fear rejection, it no longer controls me because I am better equipped to cope with it. The need and the pressure to be perfect have dwindled away, and I am actually participating in living.

As opposed to standing on the sidelines like a spectator, watching everyone else play in the game of life, I decided that it was past time for me to become involved in the game. When I was caught up in my disease, often I used my disease as an excuse and moped around feeling sorry for myself. Spinning my wheels in despair, I couldn't seem to pull myself out of the rut I was in. I was merely digging the pit deeper and deeper, and going nowhere. I had withdrawn from life, and therefore had lost opportunities to grow in mentality, capability, sophistication, sensibility, knowledge, and experience.

My retreat had left me powerless over my addictions, buried alive in a continuously sinking hole, under the increasing weight of my burdens. Many times, I tried to escape from this sinkhole to Hell, yet I did not have the proper tools in which to dig myself out. And that is what my recovery has done for me — it has provided me strong and sound tools.

Yet, just because I now have these tools, if I don't constantly dig and put forth the effort to free myself from the pit, I will sink further back. My recovery is something at which I have to diligently work everyday. It's almost like trying to grasp sunshine in my hands. As I extend my hand toward the sun, I can feel its warmth dancing within the palms of my hands. But as I tighten my hands into fists trying to clutch the sun and maintain the warmth, the light immediately disappears from my palms and the warmth quickly fades.

My recovery is similar in that I cannot grasp it in my hands to keep forever. Although I can benefit and grow in recovery, I must continue to extend open arms in order to receive the warmth it provides. My recovery is not something tangible that I can acquire once and then put up on a shelf behind other things of value only to gather dust. My recovery must be part of my everyday living and placed first above anything else. It is something that constantly needs nurturing through my continued self-awareness and rational thinking.

Although I used to do everything compulsively, based on old fears and outlandish systems of rewards and punishments, through my recovery I am now able to do things based on rational choice. Obviously, I still make mistakes and unqualified choices sometimes, but I do own up to them now. My choices are exactly that — mine, and my disease is no longer making these choices for me.

My recovery has become my homecoming, welcoming me back to the person I was born to be.

And while I've come a long way out of the darkness and into the light, I still have mountains to climb — but I also have wonderful islands to explore.

Now that I have been through treatment, I realize there are many hospitals and treatment facilities available that provide specialized services for anyone suffering from eating disorders. However, when I was still very active in my addiction I had a difficult time finding out about my choices of quality in-patient treatment that were affordable. Based on my own experiences, here is a partial list of the hospitals and programs that I have visited.

Mountain View Recovery Center
Blount Memorial Hospital
907 East Lamar Alexander Parkway
Maryville, Tennessee 37801
(615) 977-5522

Turning Point of Tampa
6301 Memorial Highway
Suite 201
Tampa, Florida 33615
1-800-397-3006 or (813) 882-3003

Remuda Ranch
Jack Burden Road
P.O. Box 2481
Wickenburg, Arizona 85358
1-800-445-1900 or (602) 684-3913

Of these three treatment facilities and of the many others that I have visited, my heart belongs to the program at Remuda Ranch. It is with great confidence in that program and the people who manage it that I recommend it for treatment. Remuda believes in total recovery and incorporates the magic of its 50 acres of desert ranch into the therapeutic process.